U.S. DEPARTMENT OF TRANSPORTATION
Federal Aviation Administration

VFR PILOT EXAM-O-GRAMS

1986 Printing

REPRINTED IN THIS BOOK BY THE AVIATION BOOK COMPANY IS A COMPLETE SET OF ALL
APPLICABLE AND AVAILABLE VFR PILOT EXAM-O-GRAMS ISSUED BY THE F.A.A.

Aviation Book Company

1640 Victory Blvd., Glendale, CA 91201

FOREWORD

Exam-O-Grams are brief explanations of
important aeronautical knowledge items. These
items include concepts and procedures that are
critical to aviation safety, common misconceptions
among airman applicants, and areas which cause
general difficulty in written tests.

VFR CRUISING ALTITUDES

Assume that you plan to make a VFR cross-country flight over terrain which has a constant elevation of 2,900 feet. After charting the course you determine that the true course is 188° and the magnetic variation is 12° E. According to the latest aviation weather reports, there is a broken layer of clouds at 7,000 feet all along the route, and the visibility is unlimited along your intended route. The winds aloft forecast indicates that the higher the altitude the more favorable the wind direction and speed. If you intend to take advantage of the most favorable wind and still comply with Federal Aviation Regulations, you should decide upon a cruising altitude of:

a.	5,500 feet MSL	c.	7,500 feet MSL
b.	6,500 feet MSL	d.	9,500 feet MSL

Analysis

1- You wish to fly as high as legally possible to take advantage of the most favorable wind.

2- The base of the broken clouds is reported in height above the surface. Therefore, the base of the clouds is approximately 2,900 feet plus 7,000 feet, or 9,900 feet above sea level.

3- Cruising altitude is a level above mean sea level (MSL), but the rules pertaining to the selection of a cruising altitude appropriate to the flight's magnetic course are applicable only when flying more than 3,000 feet above the ground.

4- This flight will be made at an altitude of more than 3,000 feet above the surface in order to take advantage of the more favorable winds at higher altitudes. Since you will be flying more than 3,000 feet above the surface, you must, according to Federal Aviation Regulations, fly at a cruising altitude appropriate to the magnetic course. In this instance the magnetic course is 176° (true course 188° - 12° E magnetic variation = 176°.)

5- A magnetic course of 176° in this case requires that you fly at an altitude (above sea level) of an odd thousand plus 500 feet.

6- In this example, you must maintain a vertical distance under the base of any cloud formation of at least 500 feet. This rules out a cruising altitude of 9,500 feet. You do not choose 5,500 feet since you want to take advantage of better tail winds at higher altitudes. You eliminate 6,500 feet because you must be at an odd thousand altitude plus 500 feet. Therefore, you select a cruising altitude of 7,500 feet, which meets legal requirements and gives you the advantage of more favorable winds.

VFR PILOT EXAM-O-GRAM° NO. 4

PREFLIGHT PLANNING FOR A VFR CROSS-COUNTRY FLIGHT
(Series 1)

1. **WHAT IS REQUIRED OF THE PILOT PRIOR TO THE FLIGHT?** FAR, Part 91.5, states in part: "Each pilot in command shall, before beginning a flight, familiarize himself with all available information concerning that flight. This information must include, for . . . . a flight not in the vicinity of an airport, weather reports and forecasts, fuel requirements, alternatives available if the planned flight cannot be completed, and any known traffic delays of which he has been advised by ATC . . . . . "

2. **WHY IS THIS REQUIRED?** Careful preflight planning, in addition to satisfying FAR, enables the pilot to make his flight with greater confidence, ease, and safety. A review of fatal accident statistics for one year shows that as a "cause factor", inadequate flight planning was second only to "failure to maintain airspeed resulting in a stall."

3. **WHAT ARE SOME SUGGESTED STEPS TO BE USED IN FLIGHT PLANNING?**

   a. Assemble materials which will be needed on the flight such as current sectional charts, and other charts, for the route to be flown; the latest AIM--Basic Flight Information and ATC Procedures, Graphic Notices and Operational Data, Notices to Airmen, Airport/Facility Directory, plotter, computer, etc. Take along charts which adjoin those for the route of flight. Thus you are prepared in case it becomes necessary to circumnavigate bad weather, or in case you inadvertently fly off the chart on which your course is drawn.

   b. On the sectional chart, draw course to be flown; study terrain; select appropriate check points; consider alert, warning, restricted, and prohibited areas and Air Defense Identification Zones; study airport information, including enroute airports that can be used in case of emergency; choose refueling stops; list frequencies of towers and navigational aids to be used and also Flight Service Stations reporting the weather.

   c. Review weather maps and forecasts, current weather reports, winds aloft forecasts, pilot weather reports, SIGMETS, AIRMETS, Notices to Airmen (NOTAMS), and other information. Although you can get weather information by telephone, it is strongly recommended that a personal visit be made to the nearest Weather Service Office, Flight Service Station, or other flight service facility.

   A chapter on Flight Planning is contained in the FAA publication, Pilot's Handbook of Aeronautical Knowledge, including a summary of flight assistance services available.

4. **WHAT FURTHER ACTION IS DICTATED BY GOOD OPERATING PRACTICES?** File a Flight Plan! This is not required by FAR but is dictated by good operating practice. It is extremely unlikely that air traffic rules can ever be written so as to eliminate the need for GOOD JUDGMENT in the planning and conduct of every flight. The pilot must make the final decision as to whether or not to make a flight. Use reasonable restraint in exercising this prerogative when preflight planning indicates the existence of marginal conditions of any kind.

BE SAFER -- FILE A FLIGHT PLAN

PREFLIGHT PLANNING FOR A VFR CROSS-COUNTRY FLIGHT
(Series 2)

1. **HOW MAY YOU OBTAIN WEATHER INFORMATION FOR PREFLIGHT PLANNING?**
    Visit your local Weather Service Office (WSO) or your nearest FAA Flight Service
    Station (FSS), or other flight service facility for a thorough weather briefing.
    The latest weather maps, area forecasts, terminal forecasts, winds-aloft
    reports, winds-aloft forecasts, advisories, hourly sequence reports, and pilot
    reports will be available. If a visit is impractical, telephone calls are welcomed.
    When telephoning, identify yourself as a pilot; state your intended route, destina-
    tion, intended time of takeoff, and approximate time en route; and, advise if you
    intend to fly only VFR.

    "FSS - CS/T and National Weather Service Telephone Numbers" section of the Airport/
    Facility contains the location and telephone numbers of weather offices and FSS
    facilities along with other pertinent information. Note the "restricted" telephone
    number listed for some Weather Service Offices on which only aviation weather infor-
    mation is given. Some Weather Service Offices have the Pilot's Automatic Telephone
    Weather Answering Service (PATWAS) which is a transcribed weather information
    service. For availability of weather information at various airports, check the
    FSS - CS/T and National Weather Service Telephone Numbers section in the back
    portion of the appropriate Airport/Facility Directory.

2. **WHAT IMPROVEMENTS HAVE BEEN MADE TO PROVIDE MORE AND BETTER
    WEATHER INFORMATION FOR PILOTS?** Equipment is provided at selected
    Flight Service Stations where weather and Notices to Airmen (NOTAMS) will be
    recorded on tapes and broadcast continuously over the low-frequency (200-400
    kHz) navigational aid facility, or VORs and VORTACs.

3. **WHAT FURTHER PREFLIGHT WEATHER PLANNING SHOULD BE DONE TO
    OBTAIN IN-FLIGHT WEATHER INFORMATION?** Refer to AIM Basic Flight Infor-
    mation and ATC Procedures manual to determine which FSS facilities along your route
    provide ENROUTE FLIGHT ADVISORY SERVICE (EFAS). Make a list of the VOR stations
    along the proposed route that provide Scheduled Weather Broadcasts, and also the
    radiobeacons (NDBs) that broadcast weather reports and Notices to Airmen.

4. **WHAT IS RECOMMENDED BY GOOD OPERATING PRACTICES?** If the preflight
    weather briefing reveals questionable or marginal weather, use reasonable
    restraint in flying VFR. File a flight plan. Maintain a close check on the
    weather through your Flight Service Stations. Be sure to close your flight plan
    upon arrival.

BE SAFER WITH A FLIGHT PLAN

PREFLIGHT PLANNING FOR A VFR CROSS-COUNTRY FLIGHT (Series 3)

The statement "NO FLIGHT PLAN FILED," which appears in many accident reports and accounts of extensive search operations for missing aircraft, indicates a degree of thoughtlessness on the part of the pilot for the safety of his flight.

> "Businessman-pilot flying daughter home from college crash lands in sparsely populated area resulting in injury to father and daughter. Rescue effected within three hours of ETA near flight plan course filed with FAA.
>
> O O O
>
> "Family of five forced down by snow storm while on flight to winter resort. No flight plan filed with FAA and 5 days later family reported missing by relatives. Search parties after covering extensive area, find bodies with no injuries-- expiration attributed to exposure."

HOW, WHEN, AND WHERE SHOULD A VFR FLIGHT PLAN BE FILED? Pilots are urged to file in person or by telephone to the nearest FSS prior to departure. Radio should be used for filing plans only if other means are not available. When filing by telephone or radio, have all the necessary information written down in the order it appears on a flight plan so that you will utilize the least amount of the controller's time and release the telephone circuit or radio frequency for someone else.

DO FEDERAL AVIATION REGULATIONS (FAR) REQUIRE THAT FLIGHT PLANS BE FILED? Regulations do not require the filing of flight plans for VFR flights unless the flight is to penetrate an ADIZ (Air Defense Identification Zone) or for flights between Mexico and the U.S. Filing at other times is entirely at the pilot's discretion, but is recommended as good operating practice.

WHY SHOULD A FLIGHT PLAN BE FILED? A flight plan not only assures prompt search and

rescue in the event you become overdue or missing, but it also permits en route stations and the destination station to render better service by having prior knowledge of your flight. It costs nothing except a few minutes of time to file a flight plan and may be the best "insurance" investment you ever made. On the other hand, failure to file could contribute to unpleasant moments during flight, or long periods of waiting for help when an emergency arises.

WHAT DISPOSITION IS MADE OF FLIGHT PLANS? When the flight plan is filed before takeoff, the FSS takes no action on it until informed of your actual departure time. The following procedures are in effect: when a VFR flight plan is filed, it will be held until one hour after the proposed departure time and then canceled unless:

1. The actual departure time is received.
2. A revised proposed departure time is received.
3. At a time of filing, the FSS is informed that the proposed departure time will be met, but actual time cannot be given because of inadequate communications.

WHAT MUST BE DONE AT THE COMPLETION OF THE FLIGHT? If a flight plan has been filed FAR requires that an arrival notice be filed at the completion of the flight or when the flight terminates at other than the planned destination. This may be done (even if no tower or FSS is located at the destination) by contacting the nearest FSS by radio prior to landing, or by telephone after landing. Contrary to popular belief, the control tower at the airport of landing does not automatically close a VFR flight plan when the landing is completed. The tower is not always aware of which aircraft were on a flight plan. It is the pilot's responsibility to file the arrival notice with the tower or FSS (simply asking by radio, telephone, or personal visit that the flight plan be closed).

TRAPPED ON TOP OF AN OVERCAST!

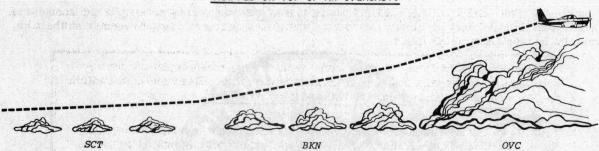

SCT   BKN   OVC

DO YOU HAVE ALL OF THE FOLLOWING REQUISITES FOR INSTRUMENT FLIGHT? (1) An Instrument Rating, (2) an aircraft fully equipped for instrument flight, and (3) recent instrument experience. If not, you should heed the following bit of advice concerning flight over an extensive overcast cloud condition -- DON'T!

SHOULD YOU AVOID FLYING VFR OVER CLOUDS ENTIRELY? No. Many times it is both practical and desirable to select a cross-country cruising altitude above a scattered cloud condition to take advantage of smoother air, improved visibility, more favorable winds, or provide for more terrain and obstacle clearance, provided (1) you have legal cloud separation for climb, cruise, and destination descent, (2) weather conditions are stable or improving, and (3) you stay alert and take immediate action if the clouds beneath you increase and the "sucker holes" start to shrink. Don't wait too long to descend or make a 180° turn (one of aviation's oldest safety devices) if the situation warrants.

WHAT OTHER PRECAUTIONS SHOULD YOU TAKE TO AVOID BEING TRAPPED ON TOP OF AN OVERCAST? (1) Prior to your cross-country flight, visit or telephone the local Weather Service Office or the nearest FAA Flight Service Station for a thorough weather briefing (see VFR Exam-O-Gram No. 5). (2) Select an altitude that will be compatible with terrain and cloud separation requirements. (3) Don't attempt VFR flight when conditions are close to VFR minimums. Remember that, with the right conditions, an overcast can form beneath you in a matter of minutes. Consider the weather, the terrain you are flying over, and allow yourself a margin of safety commensurate with your experience level. (4) While enroute, monitor appropriate frequencies for weather broadcasts, and In-Flight Weather Advisories (AIRMETS, SIGMETS, and PIREPS), or call Flight Watch. Transcribed Weather Broadcasts are also available on certain navigational aids.

WHAT SHOULD YOU DO IF YOU FIND YOURSELF IN DIFFICULTY ABOVE AN OVERCAST? You are admittedly "in distress — in a jam." Loss of ground references, probably followed by a loss of orientation, will further complicate your problem. However, you can improve your chances of avoiding disaster by following a few logical procedures. (See AIM—Basic Flight Information and ATC Procedures "Emergency Procedures" section.) For example, you should (1) Establish communications with an FSS or other ground stations and state your predicament. The personnel in these stations are well trained in assisting airmen in distress; give them a chance to help you before its too late. If necessary, they can alert available VHF/UHF Direction Finding and Radar Stations (including military stations) to stand by for possible assistance. (2) Give as much information as possible on initial contact with ATC — nature of difficulty, position (in relation to a navaid if possible), altitude, radar beacon code (if transponder equipped), weather conditions, if instrument rated or not, destination, service requested. (3) If you have trouble establishing contact with a ground station, climbing will increase the range of your VHF radio equipment and improve the chances of ground radar detection. (4) Conserve your fuel by using an economical or maximum endurance power setting. (5) Adhere to ATC instructions or information, or if not possible, advise ATC immediately that you cannot comply.

Prevention is a much better approach to this problem than the cure. If you are a VFR pilot, <u>AVOID FLYING ON TOP OF AN OVERCAST</u>.

AIRSPEED INDICATOR MARKINGS

The above airspeed indicator depicts the airspeed limitation markings of a late model single-engine airplane. How many of the airspeed questions below can you answer by studying the airspeed indicator pictured above?

1. WHAT IS THE FLAP OPERATING RANGE?

2. WHAT IS THE POWER OFF STALLING SPEED WITH THE WING FLAPS AND LANDING GEAR IN THE LANDING POSITION (Vso)?

3. WHAT IS THE MAXIMUM FLAPS EXTENDED SPEED (Vfe)?

4. WHAT IS THE NORMAL OPERATING RANGE?

5. WHAT IS THE POWER-OFF STALLING SPEED "CLEAN" - (GEAR AND FLAPS RETRACTED)?

6. WHAT IS THE MAXIMUM STRUCTURAL CRUISING SPEED (Vno)?

7. WHAT IS THE CAUTION RANGE?

8. WHAT IS THE NEVER EXCEED SPEED (Vne)?

NOTE: ANSWERS TO THE ABOVE QUESTIONS AND AN EXPLANATION OF THE STANDARD AIRSPEED INDICATOR MARKING SYSTEM APPEAR ON THE BACK OF THIS PAGE.

Airplanes manufactured after 1945 and certificated under the provisions of FAR 23 (12,500 lbs. or less) are required to have the standard system of airspeed indicator markings described in this Exam-O-Gram. In the interest of safety, it is important for you as a pilot to recognize and understand these airspeed limitation markings. This information will prove useful if you are planning to take a written test for a pilot's certificate. Current FAA written tests contain questions on this subject. A short explanation of the airspeeds and airspeed ranges you need to know follows.

★★★

NOTE: The explanations listed below are limited to simple layman's language. For additional information on airspeeds and airspeed indicator markings, refer to VFR Pilot Exam-O-Gram No. 45. For the more technical engineering nomenclature, refer to Federal Aviation Regulations, Part 23. Airspeed abbreviations and symbols are listed in FAR Part 1.

EXPLANATION OF AIRSPEED INDICATOR MARKINGS

<u>Airspeeds</u>
(See Illustration)

1. <u>FLAP OPERATING RANGE</u> (the white arc) . . . . 67 to 125 MPH (58 to 109 knots)

2. <u>POWER-OFF STALLING SPEED WITH THE WING FLAPS AND LANDING GEAR IN THE LANDING POSITION</u> (Vso). The lower A/S limit of the white arc . . 67 MPH (58 knots)

3. <u>MAXIMUM FLAPS EXTENDED SPEED</u> (Vfe). The upper A/S limit of the white arc. This is the highest airspeed at which the pilot should extend full flaps. If flaps are operated at higher airspeeds, severe strain or structural failure may result . . . . 125 MPH (109 knots)

4. <u>THE NORMAL OPERATING RANGE</u> (the green arc) . . . . 75 to 180 MPH (65 to 156 knots)

5. <u>POWER-OFF STALLING SPEED "CLEAN" - WING FLAPS AND LANDING GEAR RETRACTED</u>. The lower A/S limit of the green arc . . . . 75 MPH (65 knots)

6. <u>MAXIMUM STRUCTURAL CRUISING SPEED</u> (Vno). The upper A/S limit of the green arc. This is the maximum speed for normal operation . . . . 180 MPH (156 knots)

7. <u>CAUTION RANGE</u> (the yellow arc). You should avoid this area unless you are in smooth air . . . . 180 to 227 MPH (156 to 197 knots)

8. <u>NEVER EXCEED SPEED</u> (Vne) (the radial red line). This is the maximum speed at which the airplane can be operated in smooth air. No pilot should ever exceed this speed intentionally . . . . . . 227 MPH (197 knots)

There are other airspeed limitations <u>not marked on the airspeed indicator</u> which you should know. They are generally found on placards in view of the pilot or in the Airplane Flight Manual. One of these speeds, a very important one, is the <u>MANEUVERING SPEED</u> (Va). The <u>maneuvering speed</u> of an airplane is the maximum speed at which abrupt attitude changes can be made without exceeding the load limits. If you encounter severe turbulence, you should reduce the airspeed so that it will not exceed the specified maneuvering speed, in order to reduce the stress upon the airplane structure.

KNOW YOUR AIRSPEED LIMITATIONS -- THIS KNOWLEDGE MAY SAVE YOUR LIFE

★ ★ ★ ★

Color code for markings on the illustrations of airspeed indicators

 RED

YELLOW

GREEN

ALTIMETRY

Your altimeter is a vitally important instrument. You will agree that flight without this instrument would indeed be a haphazard undertaking -- yet, HOW WELL DO YOU KNOW YOUR ALTIMETER? Take this short quiz on altimetry; then check the answers and explanations provided.

1. Check your ability to quickly interpret the altitude by jotting down the readings of the following 6 altimeters. <u>Allow yourself 1 minute</u>.

2. Federal Aviation Regulations require that you maintain specific cruising altitudes (VFR as well as IFR) by reference to an altimeter. What do regulations require concerning the setting (or adjustment) of an altimeter?

3. If flying from very cold air (colder than standard temperatures) to very warm air, with the altimeter set to standard pressure, you should expect the altimeter to read which of the following?

       (a) <u>higher</u> than your actual altitude above sea level.
       (b) <u>lower</u> than your actual altitude above sea level.
       (c) <u>the same</u> as your actual altitude above sea level.

4. Here are 4 altitudes with which you should be familiar. Briefly give the meaning of each. (1) Indicated altitude. (2) Pressure altitude. (3) Density altitude. (4) True altitude.

5. Assume that your proposed route crosses mountains with peaks extending to 10,900 feet above sea level. Prior to crossing this range, you adjust the altimeter setting window of the altimeter to the current altimeter setting reported by a Flight Service Station located in a valley near the base of this mountain range. If you maintain an indicated altitude of 11,500 feet, can you be assured of at least 500 feet clearance above these mountain peaks?

★ ★ ★ ★ ★

ANSWERS TO QUESTIONS ON ALTIMETRY

1. (1) 7,500 ft. (2) 7,880 ft. (3) 1,380 ft. (4) 8,800 ft. (5) 12,420 ft. (6) 880 ft.

   If your altimeter is the three-pointer-type sensitive altimeter such as those pictured on the reverse side of this sheet, an orderly approach to reading the altitude is to first note the position of the smallest hand (10,000-ft. hand) to see if it is more or less than 10,000 ft.; next read the middle hand (1,000-ft. hand); and then, read the large hand (100-ft. hand). For the two-pointer altimeter, simply read the small hand first and the large hand next.

2. The altimeter should be set to the current reported altimeter setting of a station along the route of flight (Flight Service Stations, Control Towers, etc.). If your aircraft is not equipped with a radio, you should obtain an altimeter setting prior to departure if one is available, or you should adjust the altimeter to the elevation of the departure airport.

3. If flying in ~~cold~~ colder than standard air, you should expect the altimeter to indicate HIGHER than you actually are. There is an old saying -- one well worth remembering -- "WHEN FLYING FROM A HIGH TO A LOW OR HOT TO COLD, LOOK OUT BELOW!" In other words, if flying from a high pressure area to a low pressure area or into colder air, be careful because you probably aren't as high as you think -- assuming, of course, that no compensations are made for these atmospheric conditions.

4. (1) INDICATED ALTITUDE--That altitude shown on the altimeter (uncorrected for temperature).
   (2) PRESSURE ALTITUDE--The altitude indicated after the altimeter setting window is adjusted to 29.92. This altitude is used in computing density altitude, true altitude, true airspeed, etc.
   (3) DENSITY ALTITUDE--This altitude is pressure altitude corrected for nonstandard temperature variations. It is important because this altitude is directly related to the aircraft's takeoff and climb performance.
   (4) TRUE ALTITUDE--The true height of the aircraft above sea level - the actual altitude. Often you will see a true altitude expressed as: "10,900 ft. MSL"--the MSL standing for MEAN SEA LEVEL. Remember that airport, terrain, and obstacle elevations found on charts and maps are true altitudes.

5. NO, you are not assured of 500 feet clearance above these mountains. As a matter of fact, with certain atmospheric conditions, you might very well be 500 feet BELOW the peaks with this indicated altitude. To begin with, 500 feet is hardly an adequate separation margin to allow on flights over mountainous terrain -- 1,500 to 2,000 feet is recommended to allow for possible altitude errors and downdrafts.

   A majority of pilots confidently expect that the current altimeter setting will compensate for irregularities in atmospheric pressure. Unfortunately, this is not always true. Remember that the altimeter setting broadcast by ground stations is the station pressure corrected to Mean Sea Level. It does not compensate for the effect of nonstandard temperature or pressure variations.

   When flying over mountainous country, allow yourself a generous margin for terrain and obstacle clearances.

KNOW YOUR ALTIMETER

FUEL CONTAMINATION

EXCERPTS FROM AN AIRCRAFT ACCIDENT REPORT: ". . .Subsequent examination of the engine and its components revealed large deposits of foreign material, sediment, and water in the fuel strainer, carburetor bowl, and fuel pump in sufficient quantities to cause stoppage. . . Probable cause of accident: Inadequate preflight action by the pilot; subsequent engine failure due to fuel contamination. . . ."

DO YOU KNOW -- AND PRACTICE -- THE PRECAUTIONS YOU SHOULD TAKE TO AVOID FUEL CONTAMINATION?

Perhaps you do, but there are many pilots who obviously do not -- as evidenced by the number of fuel contamination-caused accidents. The modern aircraft engine is a remarkably reliable and dependable mechanism, but it will not run on water, dirt particles, and other noncombustibles. An excessive amount of contamination will displace fuel passing through the carburetor metering jets and restrict the flow of fuel; it will cause loss of power and can result in engine stoppage. Let's review this insidious problem by asking -- and answering -- a couple of rather pointed questions about this subject.

1. WHAT IS FUEL CONTAMINATION?

    Fuel is contaminated when it contains any material that was not provided under the fuel specification. This material generally consists of water, rust, sand, dust, microbial growth, and certain additives that are not compatible with the fuel or the fuel system materials.

    o o o

2. WHAT CAUSES FUEL CONTAMINATION?

    A. Storing the aircraft with partially filled fuel tanks may cause condensation and water contamination. You have, no doubt, often noticed moisture (or dew) on the outside of your aircraft early in the morning. When you noticed this, did it occur to you that moisture could form on the inside walls (above the fuel level) of your fuel tanks? Water is the worst offender in these contamination cases, and condensation inside the tank is one of the methods by which it finds its way into your fuel system.

    B. Servicing the aircraft from improperly filtered tanks, particularly small tanks or drums, is another principal source of fuel contamination. This practice frequently introduces both dirt and water into the aircraft fuel system.

    C. Contamination with other types or grades of fuel. The unintentional mixing of petroleum products can result in fuels that give unacceptable performance in the aircraft. An aircraft engine is designed to operate most efficiently on fuel of definite specifications. The use of fuels that differ from these specifications reduces operating efficiency and can lead to complete engine failure.

    Fuel servicing should be performed by trained competent personnel because of the potential hazards of inadvertently filling the tanks of a piston engine with an improper grade of gasoline or jet fuel.

3. WHAT PRECAUTIONS SHOULD THE PILOT TAKE TO AVOID FUEL CONTAMINATION?

A. PREFLIGHT ACTION: Drain a generous sample of fuel (several ounces -- not just a trickle or two) into a transparent container from each of the fuel sumps. (Notice that we specified each of the fuel sumps. This includes not only the main gascolator, but also the wing tank sumps.) Examine the sample of fuel from each sump for water and dirt contamination. Water will not mix with gasoline. If present, it will collect at the bottom of the transparent container and will be easily detected. If water or dirt appears, continue to drain from that sump until you are sure the system is clear of all water and dirt.

B. POST-FLIGHT ACTION: (1) Top off your tanks at the end of the day to avoid condensation and water contamination inside your fuel tanks. Although this is a desirable procedure to follow at the end of each flying day (assuming your loading schedule for the next day will permit a full load of fuel), it is particularly important that this is done if the aircraft is to stand idle for several days -- whether it is tied down out-of-doors or stored in a hangar. (2) Avoid, if possible, servicing your aircraft from small tanks or drums. Should this become necessary, a chamois and funnel can be used in an emergency; however, it is not recommended by FAA. Chamois is frowned upon as a fire hazard because of the possibility of a static discharge exploding the fuel vapors, yet it may remain the only means that can be used in remote areas. Imitation chamois should never be used.

NOTE: If your aircraft is not equipped with wing tank quick-drains, it is recommended they be installed, if practicable. This can make the preflight check of the wing tank sumps much more convenient, as the frequent removal and replacement of wing tank sump drain plugs can be a time-consuming operation.

C. PRECAUTIONARY MAINTENANCE ACTION: In addition to the previously discussed precautions, the following maintenance precautions should be performed on your aircraft at periodic intervals: (1) Inspect and clean the tank fuel outlet finger strainer. (2) Inspect and clean the inlet carburetor screen, and flush the carburetor bowl, if applicable.

BY FOLLOWING ALL OF THESE PRECAUTIONS, YOU CAN GREATLY REDUCE THE HAZARD OF ENGINE FAILURE DUE TO FUEL CONTAMINATION.

o o o o

To better understand the reasons for the PREFLIGHT ACTION we have recommended, let's take a brief look at an actual water contamination test conducted by FAA -- its a real eye opener!

Three gallons of water were added to the half-full fuel tank of a popular make, high-wing monoplane. After a few minutes, the fuel strainer (gascolator) was checked for water. It was necessary to drain ten liquid ounces of fuel before any water appeared. This is considerably more than most pilots drain when checking for water.

In a second test with the same aircraft in flying attitude (to simulate a tricycle geared model) the fuel system was cleared of all water; then one gallon of water was added to the half-full tank. It was necessary to drain more than a quart of fuel before any water appeared.

In both of these tests, about nine ounces of water remained in the fuel tank after the belly drain and the fuel strainer (gascolator) had ceased to show any trace of water. This residual water could be removed only by draining the tank sumps.

Two significant findings emerged from the above tests and from tests made on a plastic mockup of a similar fuel system.

1. When water was introduced into the fuel tank it immediately settled to the bottom, but did not flow down the fuel lines to the fuel strainer until all fuel was drained from the lines. Remember, each fuel tank must be turned ON to drain the tank lines through the gascolator.

2. Since it was found impossible to drain all water from the tank through the fuel lines, it was necessary to drain the fuel tank sumps in order to remove all water from the system.

● ● ● ● ●

VFR PILOT EXAM-O-GRAM   NO. 12

THE MAGNETIC COMPASS

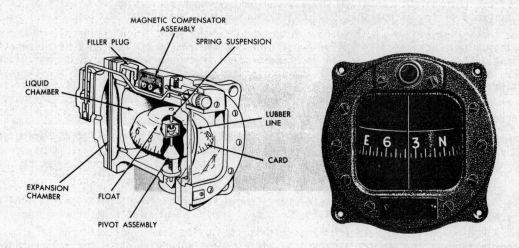

The magnetic compass, in terms of its errors, limitations, and in-flight characteristics, is one of those aeronautical subjects in which consistently large numbers of pilots do not do very well on FAA written tests. There is evidence that this veteran instrument -- it was one of the first to be installed in an aircraft -- is one of the least understood instruments in the cockpit of today's modern aircraft. Many pilots seem to operate on the premise that it is easier to ignore this instrument's characteristics rather than learn them. However, it should be remembered that (1) this is the only direction seeking instrument in most general aviation aircraft, and (2) it is mechanically a simple, self-contained unit (independent of external suction or electrical power for its operation) that is likely to remain reliable. Reliable, that is, if the pilot understands its characteristics and inherent errors.

MAGNETIC COMPASS CONSTRUCTION

The magnetic compass is simple in construction. It contains two steel magnetized needles mounted on a float. The needles are parallel with the north-seeking ends pointed in identical directions. The compass card, attached to the float, has letters to show cardinal headings (N,E,S,W) and numbers to show each 30 degrees of direction between the cardinal headings. The first and last zero of each heading number is omitted; i.e., a heading of 030° is shown as 3. Between these numbers the card is graduated for each 5°.

The float assembly, consisting of the magnetized needles and compass card, is mounted on a pivot supported on a pedestal and sealed in a chamber filled with acid-free white kerosene, or naphtha compass fluid. This fluid serves several purposes. It provides buoyancy to support part of the card's weight. It also decreases the oscillation of the card resulting from turns or turbulence. In addition, it provides lubrication at the pivot point.

WHAT ARE SOME OF THE COMPASS CHARACTERISTICS THAT THE PILOT SHOULD UNDERSTAND?

I. VARIATION — In navigation, courses drawn on aeronautical charts are based upon a relation of that course to the true geographical north pole. The magnetic compass is oriented to magnetic north, which is at a different location from true north. This angular difference between true and magnetic north is known as variation.

Lines of equal magnetic variation are called isogonic lines, and are plotted in degrees of east and west variation on aeronuatical charts. A line connecting zero degree points of variation is called the agonic line. These lines are replotted periodically on aeronautical charts to correct any change which may occur as a result of the shifting of the poles, or any changes caused by local magnetic disturbances. The pilot should understand perfectly <u>which to add and which to</u>

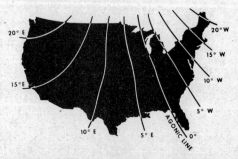

Isogonic lines connect geographical points with identical magnetic variation.

subtract when converting from true headings or courses to magnetic headings or courses and vice versa. Many pilots find such memory aids as "east is least and west is best" helpful in remembering that east is subtracted and west is added when converting from true to magnetic.

II. DEVIATION -- The deflection of the compass needles from a position of magnetic north as a result of local magnetic disturbances in the aircraft. To reduce this deviation, the compass has a compensating device consisting of small adjustable magnets. The compass deviation should be checked and compensated periodically. The errors remaining after compensating the compass should be recorded on a compass correction card which is installed in the cockpit within view of the pilot. NOTE: Avoid placing metallic objects such as metal computers, flashlights, etc., on top of the instrument panel near the magnetic compass as this practice may induce large amounts of deviation and seriously affect the instrument's accuracy. Deviation may change when different combinations of electrical equipment are turned on.

III. OSCILLATION ERROR — The erratic swinging of the compass card which may be the result of turbulence or rough pilot technique.

IV. MAGNETIC DIP — The tendency of the compass needles to point down toward the magnetic north pole because of the earth's curvature and is responsible for:

    A. Northerly Turn Error — This error is the most pronounced of the in-flight compass errors It is most apparent when turning to or from headings of north or south.

    B. Acceleration Error — This error can occur during airspeed changes. It is most apparent on headings of east and west.

As a quick review of the dip error of the compass, we invite you to accompany us on a hypothetical demonstration flight around the compass rose. Unless otherwise noted, we will limit our bank during turns to a gentle bank (15°). Also, we will assume that we are in the northern hemisphere because the characteristics which we will observe would not exist at the equator, and would be reversed in the southern hemisphere.

DEMONSTRATION NO. 1 (HEADING — NORTH; ERROR — NORTHERLY TURN ERROR)

As we start a turn in either direction from a heading of north, we notice that momentarily the compass card gives an indication of a turn opposite the direction of the actual turn. While the compass card is in a banked attitude, the vertical component of the earth's magnetic field causes the north-seeking end of the compass to dip to the low side of the turn, rotating the card and giving the pilot an erroneous turn indication. As we continue the turn toward east or west, the compass card will begin to indicate a turn in the correct direction, but will lag behind the actual turn -- at a diminishing rate -- until we are within a few degrees of east or west. An additional demonstration on a heading of north is the Slow Turn Error. With a compass indication of north, we enter a very gradual shallow banked turn (3 or 4 degrees of bank) and find it is possible to change the actual heading of the aircraft by 20° or more while still maintaining a compass indication of north.

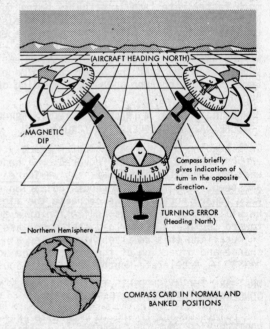

COMPASS CARD IN NORMAL AND BANKED POSITIONS

DEMONSTRATION NO. 2 (HEADING — EAST; ERROR — ACCELERATION/DECELERATION ERROR)

The Northerly Turn Error that we previously demonstrated is not apparent on an east heading (or on a west heading). However, let's see what happens when we accelerate and decelerate by changing the airspeed. With the wings level, we increase the airspeed by increasing the power setting or by lowering the nose — or both. Although we are holding the nose of the aircraft straight ahead, our compass card erroneously indicates a turn toward north. On the other hand, as we decrease the airspeed by reducing the power setting or raising the nose of the aircraft — or both, the compass will give an erroneous indication of a turn toward south. Because of the pendulous-type mounting, the side of the compass card which the pilot sees is tilted upward while accelerating and downward while decelerating during changes of airspeed. This momentary deflection of the compass card from the horizontal, results in an error that is most apparent on headings of east and west. (See illustration at the top of the next page.)

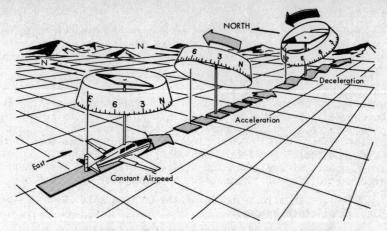

EFFECTS OF ACCELERATION/DECELERATION ERROR

DEMONSTRATION NO. 3 (HEADING — SOUTH; ERROR — NORTHERLY TURN ERROR)

In this demonstration, we again have the Northerly Turn Error problem that we encountered in Demonstration No. 1. Although the same forces that caused the erroneous indication when we banked the aircraft while on a north heading will be working against us on a heading of south, the compass indications will appear quite different. For example, as we roll into a turn in either direction from south, the compass gives us an indication of a turn in the correct direction but at a much faster rate than is actually being turned. As we continue our turn toward west or east, the compass indications will continue to precede the actual turn — but at a diminishing rate — until we are within a few degrees of west or east. It should be noted that the Acceleration/Deceleration Error is not apparent on a south heading or on a north heading.

DEMONSTRATION NO. 4 (HEADING — WEST; ERROR — ACCELERATION/DECELERATION ERROR)

On a heading of west we encounter exactly the same errors that we previously covered on a heading of east in Demonstration No. 2. As we increase the airspeed, we note an erroneous indication of a turn toward north. As we decrease the airspeed, we will get an erroneous indication of a turn toward south. A memory aid that might assist you in recalling this relationship between airspeed change and direction of the error is the word "ANDS" — Accelerate-North, Decelerate-South.

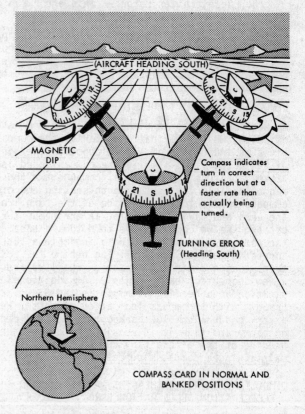

COMPASS CARD IN NORMAL AND BANKED POSITIONS

WHAT ARE THE MAIN POINTS THAT SHOULD BE REMEMBERED CONCERNING THESE DEMONSTRATIONS?

The points we are trying to emphasize are: (1) WHEN READING THE MAGNETIC COMPASS WHILE ON A NORTHERLY OR SOUTHERLY HEADING (for establishing a course, setting the gyro-driven heading indicator, etc.), REMEMBER THAT IT IS ESSENTIAL TO HAVE THE WINGS PERFECTLY LEVEL FOR SEVERAL SECONDS PRIOR TO READING THE COMPASS. (2) WHEN ON AN EASTERLY OR WESTERLY HEADING, IT IS IMPORTANT THAT THE AIRSPEED IS CONSTANT IN ORDER TO GET AN ACCURATE READING. (3) WHEN ON AN INTERMEDIATE HEADING, BOTH OF THE ABOVE CONDITIONS SHOULD BE MET. (4) THERE ARE NO ACCELERATION/DECELERATION ERRORS WHILE CHANGING AIRSPEED ON NORTH OR SOUTH HEADINGS. (5) WHEN AN AIRCRAFT IS ON AN EAST OR WEST HEADING AND A GENTLE BANKED (15°) TURN IS ENTERED THE COMPASS WILL INDICATE A TURN IN THE PROPER DIRECTION TOWARD NORTH OR SOUTH. Note: If your aircraft is equipped with a gyro-driven heading indicator, check it frequently with the magnetic compass.

NOTE: Since the north-seeking ends of the compass needles are continuously being attracted to magnetic north, the needles and compass card — unless disturbed — may be considered stationary.

When the airplane is turned to various headings, the airplane, in effect, is revolving around the stationary needles and compass card. Consequently, the pilot views that portion of the compass card on which the airplane's heading appears — through a small window in the case of the instrument.

TURNS TO HEADINGS BY REFERENCE TO THE MAGNETIC COMPASS

For the pilot who would like a general set of rules for determining the lead points for making turns by reference to the Magnetic Compass, the following is offered:

Note: The angle of bank should not exceed 15° in order to minimize dip error.

The amount of lead in recovering from a turn varies with the individual pilot's rate of rollout. As a guide, we suggest using a lead of one-half the angle of bank. For example: with a 15° angle of bank, start the rollout 7 1/2° (7° for whole numbers) before reaching the desired heading.

1. When you turn to a heading of north, the number of degrees of lead necessary is equal to the latitude plus the number of degrees required for the rollout. Example: During a left turn to a heading of north, using a 15° angle of bank, at a TAS of less than 220 knots, in a locality where the latitude is 30°N, you should start the rollout when the magnetic compass reads 037° (30° plus one-half of 15°). In a right turn to a heading of north you should start the rollout when the compass reads 323°.

2. To turn to a heading of south, turn past south the number of degrees equal to the latitude, minus the number of degrees required for the rollout. Example: When you turn to the right to a heading of south, start the rollout when the magnetic compass reads 203° (180° plus 30° minus 7°). In a left turn to a heading of south start the rollout when the compass reads 157°.

3. In a turn from north to east or west, the magnetic compass initially shows a lag. As the heading approaches the east or west heading, the magnetic compass starts to turn faster than the aircraft is turning. For this reason, you must start the rollout when the magnetic compass indicates approximately 10° ahead of 090° or 270°. Example: Start the rollout at approximately 080° when turning to east; start at 280° when turning to west.

4. In a turn from south to east or west, the magnetic compass initially shows a lead. As the heading approaches east or west, the rate of rotation of the compass card decreases and you must start the rollout only 5° ahead of 090° or 270°.

5. For intermediate headings that lie between the cardinal headings, use an approximation based on the heading's proximity to north or south, the direction of the turn, and your knowledge of the compass' lead and lag characteristics in these areas. In other words, use an "educated guesstimate."

We won't guarantee that the above methods will roll you out on the exact heading every time. At best, these are approximate methods. But it will get you reasonably close to the desired heading, and this is better than having no method at all.

> Constant vigilance for other aircraft is a must, and it is a good operating practice to have a safety pilot on board while practicing turns to magnetic compass headings. Know your magnetic compass--it will show you the way!

WEIGHT AND BALANCE

Loading the family automobile for a trip requires little serious planning. You can C-R-A-M as much luggage into the trunk as you have space, squeeze as many persons into the seats as you have room, and top off the gas tank with no thought given to Gross Weight or Center of Gravity. A similar approach to loading your "flying machine" could result in a serious accident.

WHAT IS EXCESSIVE WEIGHT? Assume that your airplane is a 4-place airplane with a baggage allowance of 120 pounds, a usable fuel capacity of 39 gallons, and an oil supply of 8 quarts. On a hypothetical flight you take on full fuel and oil servicing, toss the suitcases in the baggage compartment, and you and your three passengers eagerly climb aboard. This seems like a reasonable load, but if you had placed each of them on the scales you might have found that you and the passengers average 180 lbs. each (720 lbs.), and the four suitcases, 30 lbs. each (120 lbs.). The usable fuel load weighs 234 lbs. and the oil 15 lbs* Assume, also, that the Weight and Balance Data for the airplane shows an empty weight of 1,325 lbs. and a maximum allowable gross weight of 2,200 lbs. NOW, add the weight of the useful load to the empty weight and compare the total to the allowable gross weight. (1,089 lbs. + 1,325 lbs. = 2,414 lbs.) . . . 214 lbs. excess!

WHAT RESTRICTIONS ARE THERE ON WEIGHT AND BALANCE? In many civilian airplanes it is not possible to fill all seats, baggage compartment, and tanks, and still remain within the approved weight and balance limits. If you do not wish to leave a passenger behind (a normal reaction) you must reduce your fuel load and plan on shorter legs enroute or cut down on the baggage carried, or both. Frequently, restrictions are placed on rear seat occupancy with maximum baggage allowance aboard. By all means follow your airplane's Weight and Balance restrictions. The loading conditions and the empty weight of your particular airplane may differ from those shown in the Owner's Manual, especially if modifications have been made or equipment has been added to the original basic airplane.

IS CRUISE PERFORMANCE AFFECTED BY AN EXCESS LOAD? At normal weight, the airplane requires a certain angle of attack to maintain straight-and-level flight at a given airspeed. To sustain a heavier load at that same airspeed, the angle of attack must be greater to provide the increased lift that is necessary. More power must be added to overcome the increased drag which results from the increased angle of attack. Additional power burns more fuel, thereby reducing the range of the aircraft.

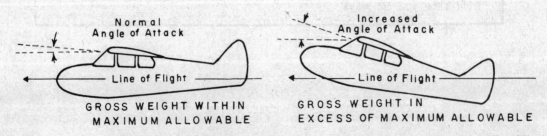

Normal Angle of Attack — Line of Flight
GROSS WEIGHT WITHIN MAXIMUM ALLOWABLE

Increased Angle of Attack — Line of Flight
GROSS WEIGHT IN EXCESS OF MAXIMUM ALLOWABLE

* NOTE: The empty weight of many new aircraft includes the weight of full oil. Refer to the Aircraft Flight Manual. Regulations have changed — See FAR 23.29, 25.29, 27.29, and 29.29.

IS CLIMB PERFORMANCE AFFECTED BY AN EXCESS LOAD? Time to climb to a given altitude is lengthened, because the angle of attack is greater and the extra thrust required to carry the additional weight limits the rate of climb and may limit the climbing speed, since this depends on the surplus power available. The additional time in climbing at the higher power setting also increases the fuel consumption.

IS "G" FORCE TOLERANCE AFFECTED? Assume that your airplane has a limit-load factor of 3.8 "G's". If the allowable gross weight is not exceeded, this means the wings can safely support 3.8 times the weight of the airplane and its contents. In accelerated flight (pull-ups, turns, turbulent air) the actual load on the wings would be much greater than the normal load, which of course results in much greater stresses in the wing structure. Overloading, therefore, has the effect of decreasing the "G" load capability of the aircraft and thus could result in the wing being stressed to the point of popped rivets, permanent distortion, or structural failure.

HOW IS AN AIRPLANE BALANCED? An airplane, like a steelyard scale, is in perfect balance when the weight is distributed in such a manner that it remains level when freely suspended. In an airplane, however, as long as the Center of Gravity lies anywhere within specified limits, balance can be maintained in flight. Flight with the CG outside of this range results in unsatisfactory or dangerous flight characteristics. Loading an airplane then, is simply a matter of distributing the load so that the CG falls within the allowable range. This can be accomplished by arranging the load in accordance with the Center of Gravity Envelope provided for each airplane.

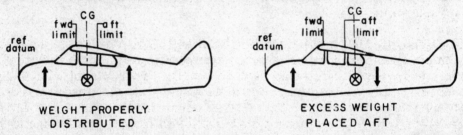

WEIGHT PROPERLY DISTRIBUTED   EXCESS WEIGHT PLACED AFT

DOES IMPROPER LOAD DISTRIBUTION AFFECT SAFETY? YES! When loading conditions cause the Center of Gravity to fall outside allowable limits, stability is adversely affected and erratic control forces may develop. Stalling speed, takeoff distance, and landing speed may be increased to the point of actual danger.

Due to the size of many baggage compartments there might be a tendency to fill them to capacity, ignoring the placarded baggage weight limitations. This could produce a Center of Gravity aft of allowable limits creating a highly dangerous flight condition. The result would be a nose high attitude which could lead to a stall from which recovery might not be effected due to inadequate elevator control.

AN AIRPLANE'S BEHAVIOR IN THE AIR
IS DEPENDENT ON WEIGHT AND BALANCE!

VOR (SERIES I)

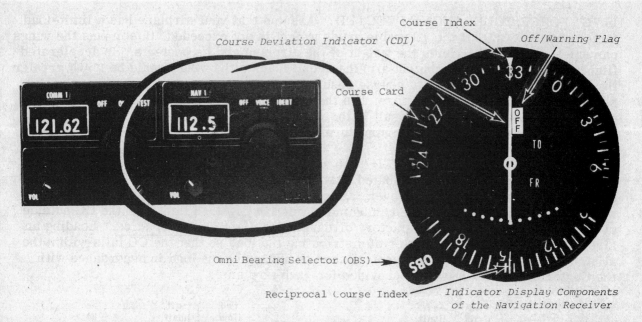

Course Index

Course Deviation Indicator (CDI)

Off/Warning Flag

Course Card

Omni Bearing Selector (OBS) →

Reciprocal Course Index

*Indicator Display Components
of the Navigation Receiver*

The purpose of this Exam-O-Gram is to explain some of the uses of the VOR receiver equipment and to discuss certain areas of misunderstanding and confusion concerning VOR navigation.

WHAT IS THE MEANING OF VOR? -- VOR is the abbreviation for VHF Omnidirectional Range. The terms VOR, omni, and omnirange are used synonymously. An omnidirectional range derives its name from the Latin word OMNIS meaning "all" -- it is a ground station that provides directional guidance in all directions. A VORTAC facility consists of two components, VOR and TACAN. The military system TACAN, when incorporated with VOR becomes a navigational aid called VORTAC. VORTACs provide distance information for use with airborne Distance Measuring Equipment (DME).

WHAT IS THE FUNCTION OF THE INDICATOR DISPLAY COMPONENTS OF A VOR RECEIVER?

1- Omni Bearing Selector (OBS) - Permits the selection of any one of 360 magnetic courses TO or FROM a VOR station. The OBS knob rotates the omnibearing dial (course card). It is also referred to as the Course Selector (CS).

2- Course Deviation Indicator (CDI) - A vertical needle that moves to the left or right to display the position of the selected VOR course relative to the position of the aircraft. When the aircraft is located on the selected course the CDI needle is centered regardless of the aircraft heading.

3- TO-FROM Indicator - Indicates the position of the aircraft in relation to the VOR station, when used in conjunction with the course selected and the CDI. It shows whether the course selected under the course index, if intercepted and flown, will take the aircraft TO or FROM the station.

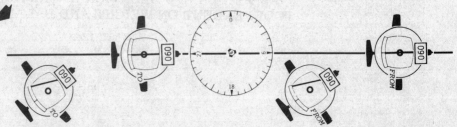

4- OFF/Warning Flag - Indicates when the system is not functioning or that the OMNI signal is unsuitable for navigation.

5- SOME OF THE USES OF THE RECIPROCAL COURSE INDEX -- (a) It indicates the reciprocal of a selected course. When desiring to reverse course (180°), the new course can be determined by
referring to the numbers which appear under the reciprocal course index. (b) When the CDI
needle is centered with a TO indication the <u>radial</u> being flown can be determined by reading
the course that appears by the reciprocal course index.

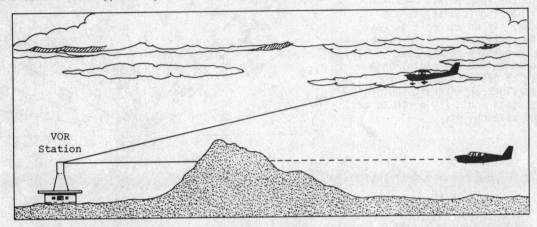

A disadvantage of VOR is its limited reception distance at low altitude in
mountainous areas, due to line-of-sight transmission characteristics. Note
below the restrictions listed for certain radials of the Alamosa VORTAC.

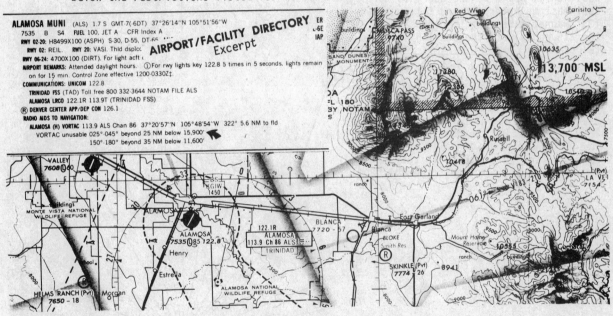

WHAT IS A RADIAL? It is a magnetic bearing (course) extending from the station. The VOR provides 360 courses which radiate from the station like spokes from the hub of a wheel. These
courses, known as radials, are identified by their magnetic bearing from the station. This means
that an aircraft can fly away from the station on any one of 360 radials or inbound to the station on any one of the 360 different magnetic bearings. On navigation charts, courses are published as directions outbound from the VOR stations (radials).

WHAT IS PROPER SENSING? Simply this -- if the CDI needle is to the right, the desired course is
to the right; if the CDI needle is to the left, the desired course is to the left. In other
words, the desired course is on the same side as the CDI needle deflection. (NOTE: With reverse
or opposite sensing, if the CDI needle is deflected to the right the desired course is on the
left.)

HOW CAN YOU BE SURE THAT THE CDI NEEDLE IS GIVING PROPER SENSING? By ensuring that the heading
of the aircraft is approximately the same as the course that appears under the course index.

WHEN DOES THE CDI NEEDLE GIVE REVERSE SENSING? When the aircraft heading and selected course are
approximately reciprocals (actually, anytime the angle between heading and selected course is
greater than 90°).

To fly inbound to a VOR station on a particular radial, it is necessary to have the OBS course set to the appropriate reciprocal bearing (course) to the station. If an aircraft is west of the station on the 270 radial it is necessary to fly east (inbound on the 270 radial on a course of 090°) to arrive over the station; an aircraft south of the station would fly north to get to the station, etc.

For Example:

Airplane A is located on the 315 radial which is <u>northwest</u> of the station. To fly <u>directly</u> to the station from this position it would be necessary to turn southeast to intercept and follow the 135° magnetic bearing (reciprocal of the 315 radial) to the station -- (Airplane B).

However, the pilot of Airplane A may elect to fly to the station without being precisely inbound on the 315 radial. This could be done by turning the airplane left or right to a heading of 135°; rotating the OBS until the CDI needle is centered with a TO indication; and then tracking inbound to the station on whatever course centers the CDI needle.

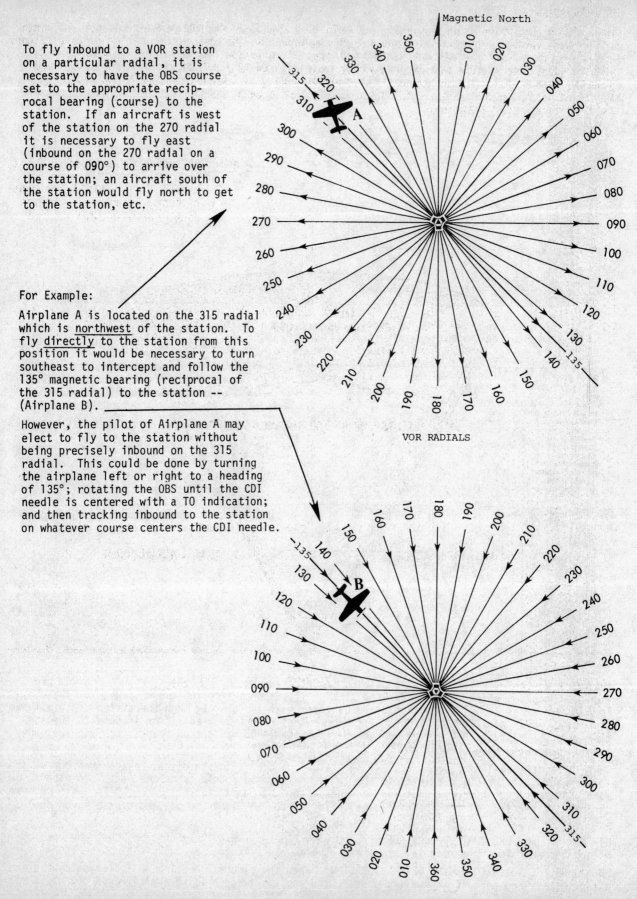

VOR RADIALS

MAGNETIC BEARINGS (COURSES) TO THE STATION

STATION PASSAGE

The <u>cone of confusion</u> is encountered just before passing over the VOR station. Since the width of the cone varies with altitude, the actual time spent in the cone varies according to altitude and groundspeed. As the aircraft enters the cone of confusion, the CDI needle may swing from side to side, the TO-FROM indicator may fluctuate between TO and FROM, and the course warning flag may appear. For timing purposes, station passage occurs when the TO-FROM indicator makes the first positive change to FROM. After leaving the cone of confusion, the CDI stabilizes and resumes its normal indications.

NOTE: FAA and ICAO standards require that the unreliable area not exceed 60° in width. The cone of confusion of most stations is smaller than this.

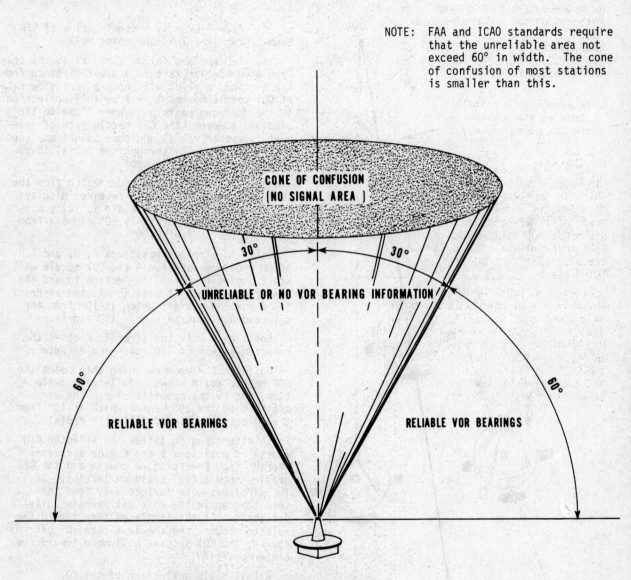

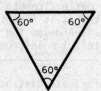

In estimating the approximate width of the cone of confusion consider an equilateral triangle with three sides of equal length and three 60° angles.

Altitude AGL	Approximate Width
6,000 feet	6,000 feet
10,000 feet	10,000 feet
18,000 feet	18,000 feet (3.4 SM)

VOR (SERIES 2)

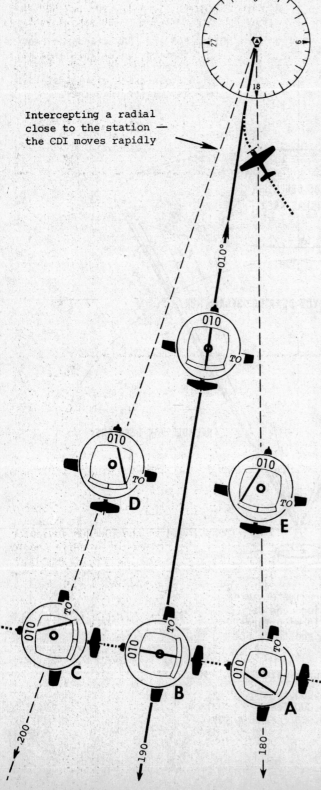

Intercepting a radial
close to the station —
the CDI moves rapidly →

This Exam-O-Gram is a continuation of VFR Exam-O-Gram (No. 15) concerning VOR.

To intercept and follow a radial to the station when the aircraft is a great distance from the station, a pilot will note a very slow rate of CDI needle movement -- from full deflection to the centered position. When close to the station, however, the CDI needle rate of movement is rather rapid, and some pilots may tend to overshoot or fly through the radial they are attempting to intercept.

The CDI needle displays deviation from the selected course. Most VOR receiver displays are adjusted so the CDI needle is fully displaced when the aircraft is 10° or more from the selected course.

Refer to airplane positions A, B, and C. After crossing position A the CDI needle will start moving from full deflection toward the center position. At position A, the aircraft is on the 180 radial, which is 10° from the selected 010° course - or - 190 radial.

Position B - As the aircraft crosses the selected course of 010° the needle centers.

Position C - Upon reaching this point the CDI needle again shows a full-scale deflection, but to the opposite side. The aircraft is on the 200 radial which is 10° from the selected course of 010° (190 radial).

In attempting to follow the selected 010° course at positions D and E, the airplanes are 10° from the selected course and the CDI needles show a full-scale deflection. If the airplanes move farther away from the selected course the CDIs will remain fully deflected. If the airplanes turn toward the selected course and are less than 10° off course, the CDI needles will move toward the center position.

A full-scale deflection of the CDI needle = approximately 1,000 feet per nautical mile from the station. For example, a full-scale deflection of the CDI in an aircraft that is 5 nautical miles from the station means the aircraft is approximately 1 mile from the selected course.

Distance From Station	Approximate Distance Either Side of Course
1 nautical mile	1,000 feet
5 nautical miles	1 mile
25 nautical miles	5 miles
50 nautical miles	10 miles

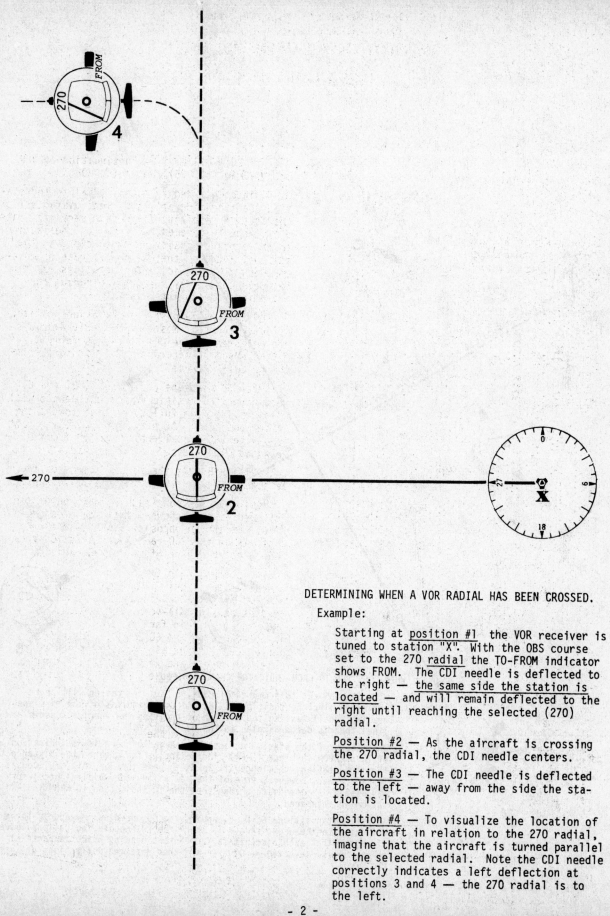

DETERMINING WHEN A VOR RADIAL HAS BEEN CROSSED.

Example:

Starting at <u>position #1</u> the VOR receiver is tuned to station "X". With the OBS course set to the 270 <u>radial</u> the TO-FROM indicator shows FROM. The CDI needle is deflected to the right — <u>the same side the station is located</u> — and will remain deflected to the right until reaching the selected (270) radial.

<u>Position #2</u> — As the aircraft is crossing the 270 radial, the CDI needle centers.

<u>Position #3</u> — The CDI needle is deflected to the left — away from the side the station is located.

<u>Position #4</u> — To visualize the location of the aircraft in relation to the 270 radial, imagine that the aircraft is turned parallel to the selected radial. Note the CDI needle correctly indicates a left deflection at positions 3 and 4 — the 270 radial is to the left.

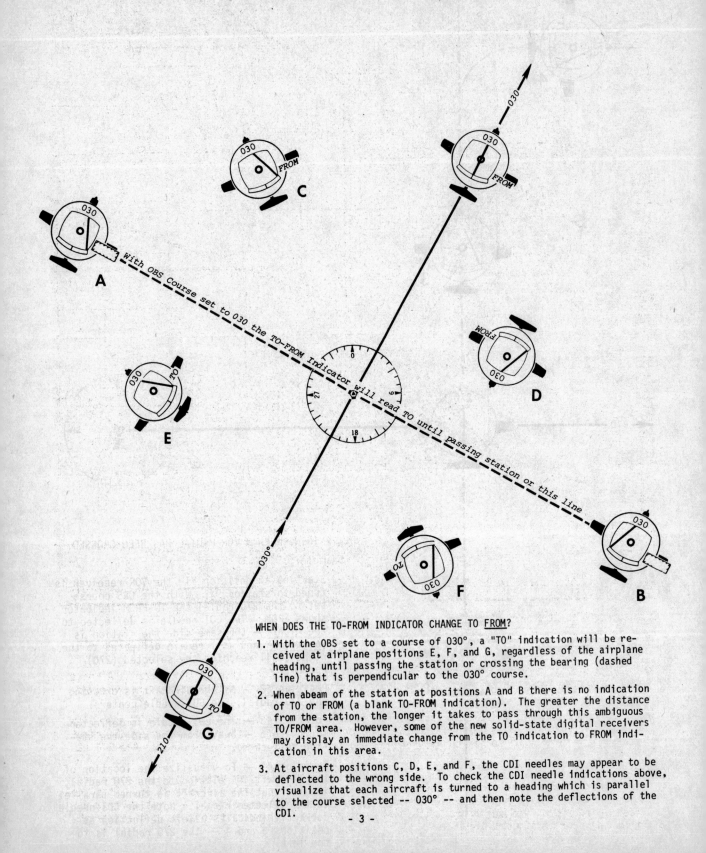

With OBS Course set to 030 the TO-FROM Indicator will read TO until passing station or this line

WHEN DOES THE TO-FROM INDICATOR CHANGE TO <u>FROM</u>?

1. With the OBS set to a course of 030°, a "TO" indication will be received at airplane positions E, F, and G, regardless of the airplane heading, until passing the station or crossing the bearing (dashed line) that is perpendicular to the 030° course.

2. When abeam of the station at positions A and B there is no indication of TO or FROM (a blank TO-FROM indication). The greater the distance from the station, the longer it takes to pass through this ambiguous TO/FROM area. However, some of the new solid-state digital receivers may display an immediate change from the TO indication to FROM indication in this area.

3. At aircraft positions C, D, E, and F, the CDI needles may appear to be deflected to the wrong side. To check the CDI needle indications above, visualize that each aircraft is turned to a heading which is parallel to the course selected -- 030° -- and then note the deflections of the CDI.

- 3 -

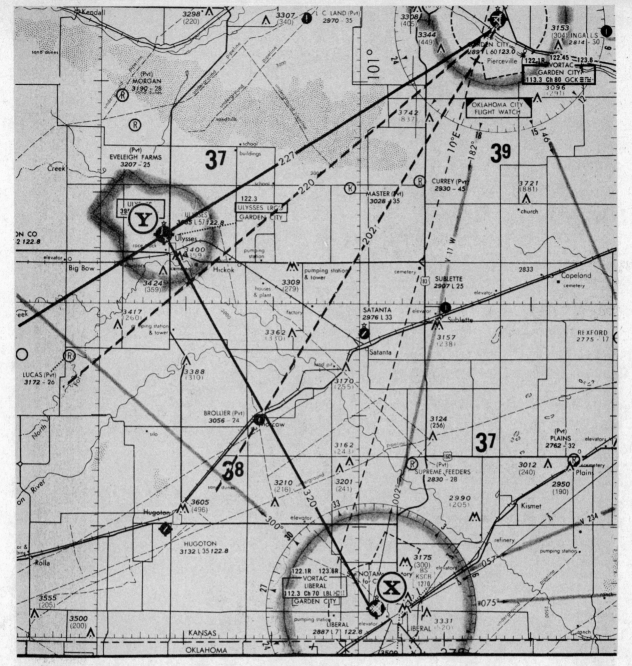

USING VOR CROSS BEARINGS TO LOCATE AN AIRPORT

● Assume that you are tracking outbound from Airport "X" to Airport "Y" on the 320 radial of Liberal VORTAC.

● Tune in another station (such as Garden City VORTAC) off to one side of the route to Airport "Y," and draw lines on the chart by extending radials from that station across the proposed route and destination airport.

● En route, the OBS can be rotated to selected radials (such as the 202 and 220) of Garden City VORTAC to determine when they are crossed. When the selected radials are drawn on the chart they can then be used to determine progress along the route, the groundspeed, or the ETA at Airport "Y."

● Upon reaching the 227 radial of Garden City VORTAC, with precision tracking along the route, the aircraft should be directly over Airport "Y" or within gliding distance of it. This procedure should help the pilot avoid flying beyond the destination airport — particularly in restricted visibility conditions, at night, or when the airport is difficult to distinguish from the surrounding terrain.

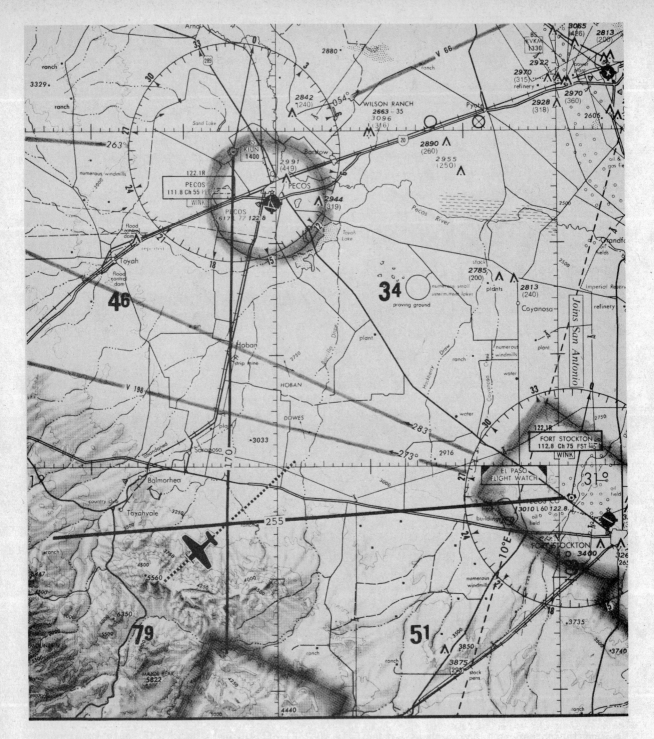

USING CROSS BEARINGS TO LOCATE POSITION

- Suppose in the illustration above the pilot of the airplane knows that he is somewhere in the vicinity of Pecos and Fort Stockton, but is not certain of the exact position. The pilot tunes to the Pecos and Fort Stockton VORs and rotates the OBS to determine which radial of each station will center the CDI needle with a FROM indication.

- Lines can then be drawn on the aeronautical chart, extending along the radials from each station (170 radial from Pecos and 255 radial from Fort Stockton). The point on the chart at which the two radials intersect is the approximate position of the aircraft at the time the cross-bearings were taken.

POOR GUY...

COMMON MISCONCEPTIONS (Series #1)

The following remarks are actual excerpts from a pilot's written report of an accident in which he was involved.

"I was climbing at an airspeed of 60 mph. I started a climbing turn to the right. The wind now became a cross wind instead of a head wind. This (lack of head wind) caused the airplane to stall -- to recover from the stall I turned the airplane back into the wind . . . (Later) I was in a quartering tailwind from the right. . . Went into a second stall. . . This is all I remember."

This pilot had over 100 hours, yet stalled and crashed due to an apparent misuse of controls at a slow airspeed (high angle of attack). The inspector who took this pilot's statement decided to pursue this theory with a group of student pilots. He posed this question to them.

"If the aircraft's stalling speed was 60 mph and you were flying at an airspeed of 70 mph into a 30 mph wind, what would happen if you maintained this airspeed of 70 mph but turned downwind?" Five of the six students said the airplane would stall.

IS THIS ANSWER CORRECT? No.

DOES THE STALLING SPEED OF AN AIRPLANE DEPEND UPON THE AIRSPEED OR THE GROUNDSPEED? The airspeed.

DOES THE DIRECTION OF THE WIND HAVE ANY EFFECT ON THE AIRSPEED OF AN AIRCRAFT IN FLIGHT? No.

Now to summarize our point, airspeed is the only speed which holds any significance for an airplane. Once it is off the ground, an airplane feels nothing but its own speed through the air. It makes absolutely no difference what its speed happens to be in relation to the ground. The aircraft in flight feels no wind. It simply proceeds, operating with the same mechanical efficiency, upwind, downwind, crosswind, or in no wind at all. (NOTE: We are referring here to a steady wind. Turbulence, gusts, or wind shears can lead to stalls even though airspeed is being maintained above the normal stalling speed. In such conditions it is wise to add a safe margin to normal climbout or approach speeds.)

Based on the performance of many applicants on the Private Pilot Written Test, here are some of the other more common misconceptions.

IF IT IS NECESSARY TO CLEAR OBSTRUCTIONS IMMEDIATELY AFTER TAKEOFF, SHOULD YOU USE BEST ANGLE-OF-CLIMB SPEED OR BEST RATE-OF-CLIMB SPEED? Best angle-of-climb speed. Simply stated, the difference is this. The best angle-of-climb speed produces the greatest climb in a given distance; the best rate-of-climb speed produces the greatest climb in a given time. Distance, of course, is the determining factor for takeoff obstruction clearance.

DO ALL WIND REPORTS INDICATE A TRUE DIRECTION? No. The wind direction, as reported by a control tower in pilot instructions, is magnetic. All other wind directions (Sequence Reports, Terminal Forecasts, Winds Aloft Forecasts, etc.) are true.

WHAT IS THE HEIGHT OF A CLOUD CEILING BASED ON? The height of the clouds above the ground, not the height above sea level (MSL). For example, let's examine the following weather report: ABQ M30 OVC. The station is Albuquerque, N.M., which has an elevation of 5,352 feet above sea level. The ceiling is reported as a 3,000-foot overcast. Using the current Albuquerque altimeter setting, your altimeter would indicate approximately 8,352 feet at the base of the clouds when over the airport, but your height above the ground would be 3,000 feet. As a word of caution, the 10,000-foot-plus mountains a few miles east of the city would probably extend up into the clouds since this ceiling report is based on an observation taken over the airport.

WHICH IS THE MORE DENSE -- MOIST AIR OR DRY AIR? Dry air. It is generally understood that high temperatures and high elevations result in a higher density altitude, but there seems to be a general impression that moist air has the reverse effect. The common misconception is that moist air is heavier than dry air. This is not true! Water vapor weighs less than an equal amount of dry air. A dry parcel is therefore denser and heavier than a moist parcel. Since both engine and aircraft performance decrease with an increase in density altitude, you should remember that high relative humidities (small spreads between temperature and dew point), especially on hot summer days, will result in longer takeoff runs.

IS AN AIRCRAFT CRUISING VFR AT 5,500 FEET MSL ALWAYS GOVERNED BY THE VFR CRUISING ALTITUDES REQUIREMENTS? Not necessarily. The rule pertains to aircraft operated in level cruising flight at more than 3,000 feet above the surface. The aircraft in this case (5,500 feet MSL) might be operating above a surface elevation of 3,500 feet and this rule would not apply.

* * * * *

These are, by no means, all of the common misconceptions that prevail among student pilots, but as we stated earlier, a trend has become apparent in the Private Pilot Written Examination results which highlights these that are discussed. Additional misconceptions are discussed in Exam-O-Gram No. 26.

CEILING & VISIBILITY

An analysis of common mistakes on written examinations indicates that many applicants are improperly interpreting the ceilings and visibilities reported on hourly weather reports (sequence reports).

How about you? Do you really know what a ceiling is - what visibility is - and how both are reported??

A. CEILING:

1. Is defined as the "lowest layer of clouds or obscuring phenomena <u>aloft</u> that is reported as 'broken' (.6 to .9 coverage), or 'overcast' (more than .9 coverage) and not classified as 'thin'; or the height ascribed to <u>surface-based</u> obscuring phenomena not classified as 'partial'." This simply means that -

    a. The lowest cloud coverage reported as broken or overcast constitutes a ceiling <u>except</u> when a minus sign precedes the cloud layer contraction (-BKN, -OVC). When this occurs, that particular layer <u>does not</u> constitute a ceiling.

    b. If the sky is reported as completely obscured (X) by a phenomena extending to the surface (e.g., fog, dust, heavy precipitation), the ceiling is the vertical visibility into the obscuration.

    c. If the sky is partially obscured (-X) it <u>does not</u> constitute a ceiling and no height will be given for this partial obscuration.
    <u>Example</u>: OKC -X 18 SCT M35 OVC, etc.

    d. Scattered clouds (SCT) <u>do not</u> constitute a ceiling.

2. For practical purposes, ceiling is the lowest height above the surface at which the total cloudiness between that level and the surface (as seen by a ground observer) covers more than half the sky.

    NOTE: The contractions CLR, SCT, BKN, and OVC have replaced the symbols ◯, ◑, ◍, and ⊕.

3. Ceiling may be classified in several ways. This classification is shown by a letter which precedes the ceiling height. Some of the more important of these letters are:

M = measured   E = estimated   W = indefinite

If one of these letter symbols does not precede the cloud contraction or if thin broken or overcast clouds, or a partial obscuration exists, there is no ceiling. Example: CBI -X 1Ø SCT 14 -BKN 14Ø -OVC 5H, etc. means that no official ceiling exists at Columbia, Missouri.

B. CLOUDS:

1. In sequence reports the heights of cloud-base levels are given in feet above the ground, not above sea level. Note that the clouds are at approximately 1000 feet at station "A" and 6000 feet at station "B" in the illustration on the first page.

2. The figure for the height of the cloud base above the surface precedes each sky coverage contraction.

3. The last two digits of the cloud height are omitted; i. e., 1 means 100 feet, 14 means 1400 feet, and 140 means 14,000 feet.

4. Clouds are reported in ascending order of height whether or not they constitute a ceiling.

5. Surface-based total obscurations (phenomena other than clouds such as fog, precipitation, dust, smoke, or haze) are not reported as clouds since this would be misleading but they are reported with a height value.

Example: BUF W15 X 3/4S-F, etc., means that at Buffalo there is a vertical visibility of 1500 feet into a total obscuration. A definite cloud base cannot be seen from the ground.

C. VISIBILITY:

1. Visibility is the greatest distance on the earth's surface at which prominent objects can be seen and identified. This distance is not always the same in all directions. Therefore, the value for prevailing visibility (which is a ground visibility only) is based on surface observations and is stated in the hourly sequence reports. Prevailing visibility is always reported in statute miles and is the greatest surface visibility attained or surpassed throughout at least one-half of the horizon circle, but not necessarily continuous or for all of the horizon circle.

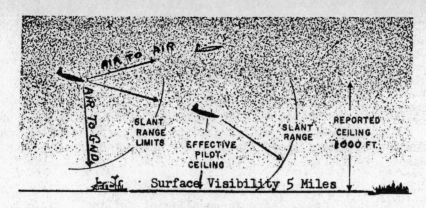

Types of Visibility in Aviation

All pilots should clearly understand that sequence report visibility may be much greater than either air to air, or slant range visibility, particularly when low ceilings and/or obscurations prevail.

2. Fractional values for visibility such as $1\frac{1}{4}$, $1\frac{1}{2}$, $2\frac{1}{2}$, etc., appear as 1 1/4, 1 1/2, 2 1/2, on the hourly sequence report because the teletype machines do not have fractions.
   <u>Example</u>: CLE M12 BKN 2Ø OVC 2 1/2R-F Ø71/39/37/ØØØØ/974

3. It is not always possible to look at the visibility as reported in the main body of the teletype report and obtain complete information concerning surface visibility at the station because:

   a. If, in some direction from the station, there is a significant variation from the prevailing visibility, this variation will be found only in the <u>remarks section</u>.
      <u>Example</u>: PIT E18 OVC 4S-K Ø31/32/3Ø/ØØØØ/962/VSBY N 1 means that the reported visibility is reduced to 1 mile to the north.

4. Weather occurring at the time of observation is also reported through use of letter symbols. These symbols <u>follow</u> the visibility as reported in statute miles. Some of the more common of these symbols are:

   R=Rain; S=Snow; T=Thunderstorm; RW=Rain showers; A=Hail; IP=Ice pellets

5. Except for thunderstorms, hail, and ice crystals, the intensity of weather is shown by:

   a. A plus sign (+) <u>following</u> the symbol to indicate "heavy".
   b. A minus sign (-) <u>following</u> the symbol to indicate "light".
   c. A double minus sign (--) following the symbol to indicate "very light".
   d. The <u>absence</u> of any sign indicates the intensity is "moderate".

   <u>Example</u>: STL 5 SCT E1Ø OVC 2R--S-K etc., which indicates that St. Louis has very light rain, light snow, and smoke. Note that these signs apply only to the weather and not to the obstructions to vision.

LAX -4 -SCT 14 -BKN 25Ø -OVC 4HK 196/66/63/ØØØØ/Ø11/VSBY N 2

A. Based on the above report --

1. IS THERE A PARTIAL OBSCURATION AT 400 FEET OR SCATTERED CLOUDS AT 400 FEET?
    Ans. No. Height values are not assigned to partial obscurations, and the
    figures for cloud heights above the ground precede the sky coverage contrac-
    tion for those clouds; therefore, the figure 4 must refer to the scattered
    clouds.

2. WHAT IS THE CEILING? Ans. There is no official ceiling. No letter precedes
    the cloud contractions and all cloud coverage is reported as thin (-).

3. WHAT IS THE VISIBILITY? Ans. Prevailing surface visibility is 4 statute
    miles with haze and smoke, but to the north visibility is only 2 statute
    miles.

4. SHOULD A PILOT EXPECT HIS SLANT RANGE AIR TO GROUND VISIBILITY TO BE 4 MILES
    AT LOS ANGELES? Ans. No. Under the circumstances of obscuration, partial
    haze and smoke, it is probably less.

DEN 1Ø SCT M3Ø BKN 8Ø OVC 2VFK Ø31/75/65/11Ø5/962/VSBY 1V3

B. Based on the above report --

1. WHAT IS THE CEILING? Ans. Measured 3000 feet above the surface.

2. AT 7500 FEET MEAN SEA LEVEL OVER DENVER, COLORADO, WOULD THE PILOT BE ABOVE OR
    BELOW THE CLOUDS REPORTED AT 3000 FEET? Ans. Below the clouds. At 7500 feet
    MSL he is approximately 2200 feet above the ground at Denver.

3. SHOULD A PILOT INTERPRET THIS REPORT TO MEAN THAT HE WILL FIND .9 OR MORE CLOUD
    COVER AT 8000 FEET ABOVE THE SURFACE? Ans. No. While it is possible that
    this situation actually exists, it is also true that such may not be the case
    at all. If there actually exists, visible from the ground, .5 coverage at
    1000 feet, .4 coverage at 3000 feet, and .1 coverage at 8000 feet, it would be
    reported as 1Ø SCT M3Ø BKN 8Ø OVC. The combination of clouds at various
    levels may make it impossible for the ground observer to determine the actual
    percentage of cloud cover for all except the lowest level.

C. WHY SHOULD A PILOT BE EXTREMELY CAREFUL IN INTERPRETING CEILING VALUES, PARTICULARLY
    IN MOUNTAINOUS AREAS? Ans. If he does not he may "booby trap" himself into expect-
    ing an adequate ceiling when it does not exist! He must always relate surface
    elevation at the reporting station to terrain elevation along his flight route.
    The diagram on Page 1 illustrates what can happen to a 6000-foot ceiling when the
    surface elevation changes. He must also be aware that there are wide enroute
    variations from the reported ceilings (and visibility) even if there is no signif-
    icant change in terrain elevation.

FLYING INTO UNFAVORABLE WEATHER

How many times have you overheard or perhaps made similar statements yourself - "Let's go, we don't need weather, we'll make it okay." All too often a departing pilot merely glances at or completely ignores weather reports and forecasts because of a biased opinion that "weathermen never hit it right anyway". True, ceiling and visibility reports are sometimes estimated and a forecast is for conditions likely to occur; but if you don't utilize this information, your flight may be full of unhappy surprises. Accident investigation statistics continue to reveal "flight into unfavorable weather" as the chief cause of VFR fatal accidents. Results of FAA written examinations confirm that many pilots lack an adequate understanding of weather information.

WHY DO PILOTS FLY INTO UNFAVORABLE WEATHER?

1. GO-ITUS -- "I gotta get there . . ."; "I don't have time to wait." This is a condition that usually converts HOT PILOTS into COLD BODIES, and is a most difficult "disease" to cure. This attitude can be controlled only through sound reasoning and judgment by the individual.

2. MISINTERPRETATION OF FORECASTS AND REPORTS -- "It looks like VFR . . ."; "aw, it's good enough." Applicant performance on FAA written examinations indicate that the problem lies not in reading the data, but in knowing just what it means in terms of expected weather conditions.

3. FAILURE TO KEEP ABREAST OF WEATHER CHANGES -- Weather conditions do change, and the best way to keep informed en route is to listen to in-flight advisories and scheduled broadcasts.

4. IGNORING IN-FLIGHT WEATHER SIGNS -- "It's just a little shower . . ."; "just a few puffs of clouds." Rarely does weather suddenly go bad with no warning. Signs of deteriorating weather should be learned and observed by the VFR pilot.

ARE YOU "WEATHER WISE" OR OTHERWISE?

DOES A STATION REPORT OF VFR CEILING MEAN EN ROUTE VFR? NO, the ceiling reported is the height above the reporting point only. It must also be related to the surrounding and en route terrain to determine if adequate VFR separation can be maintained between stations. (See Exam-O-Gram 20.) Additionally, unreported conditions between stations may be lower than those reported at the stations.

IS REPORTED VISIBILITY THE SAME AS VISIBILITY ALOFT? NO, the reported visibility is the visibility at the surface only. Conditions aloft may restrict flight visibility more or less than that reported. (See Exam-O-Gram 20.) Cockpit visibility in precipitation is further reduced by rain, drizzle, or snow spreading over the windshield. Forward visibility in a light snowfall may be zero due to the relative horizontal movement of the snow. Sunlight reflecting off haze or dust aloft reduces the visibility considerably.

WHAT CAN BE LEARNED FROM TEMPERATURE REPORTS? High temperatures reduce takeoff and landing performance. Low temperatures reflect the approximate freezing level and the areas of possible icing in precipitation. Sudden temperature changes reveal the relative position of a front and its associated weather.

WHAT IS THE SIGNIFICANCE OF DEW POINT? Specifically, a dew point value relatively close (2° - 5°) to the air temperature is indicative of the probability of fog, low clouds, or precipitation.

WHY SHOULD THE REPORTED WIND DATA BE NOTED? The velocity and direction of the surface wind should be related to the runway at the point of intended landing to determine the degree of cross wind. Wind data also reflects the degree of turbulence to expect. A sudden shift in direction often reveals the position of frontal weather relative to a station.

OF WHAT VALUE IS THE ALTIMETER SETTING? Correct cruising altitudes and adequate vertical clearance are dependent on the application of altimeter settings. A rapid and continual drop in pressure (altimeter setting) forewarns of approaching inclement weather.

WHAT IS A PIREP AND WHERE IS IT FOUND? A PIREP is a report of weather conditions at flight altitude, particularly between stations, <u>seen by the pilot</u> instead of the ground observer. Reports are often broadcast, and a pilot report summary is disseminated hourly to stations by teletype. Cloud base and top reports are found in the Remarks section of sequence reports.

ARE <u>YOU</u> GETTING THE REAL PICTURE FROM FORECASTS AND REPORTS? Only when the above are considered in analyzing forecasts and reports will you have the full story.

WHAT ARE SOME OF THE WEATHER SIGNPOSTS AND THEIR WARNINGS?

<u>Blowing Dust</u> -- turbulence, poor visibility at low levels, particularly into the sun.

<u>Low Layer of Haze</u> -- possible fog or stratus cloud in early morning or late evening; poor visibility, particularly into the sun.

<u>Light Puffs of Clouds at Low Levels</u> -- probable fog or stratus cloud, particularly in early morning or late evening.

<u>Ragged Cloud Base</u> -- turbulence, erratic visibility, possible precipitation.

<u>Bulbous Cloud Base</u> -- turbulence, possible precipitation, conducive to TORNADOES.

<u>Roll-Type Clouds</u> -- DANGEROUS turbulence, dust and poor visibility, hazardous landing conditions, subsequent precipitation.

<u>Line of Heavy Dark Clouds</u> -- SEVERE turbulence, dust and poor visibility, hazardous landing conditions, precipitation, hail.

<u>Opening in Wall of Dark Clouds (SUCKER HOLE)</u> -- DANGEROUS turbulence, possible precipitation and poor visibility as the hole is entered.

<u>Gradual Lowering and Thickening of the Ceiling</u> -- inadequate terrain clearance, possible widespread precipitation, and fog.

<u>Near Freezing Temperature</u> -- poor visibility in precipitation with ice forming on the windshield as well as the aircraft structure.

THE 180° TURN IS AVIATION'S BEST SAFETY DEVICE -- <u>IF</u> USED <u>PRIOR</u> TO BEING ENVELOPED BY ADVERSE WEATHER. DON'T BE A "PUSHER" IN THE hope THAT THE WEATHER WILL GET BETTER!

POTENTIAL MID-AIR COLLISIONS

Analyses of answers to Pilot and Ground Instructor Written Tests indicate that many applicants do not fully understand several areas in Regulations and procedures that were devised as safety measures for VFR flying. Two of the areas will be covered in this Exam-O-Gram that seem to give applicants the most difficulty. They concern VFR Altitudes/Flight Levels in controlled and uncontrolled airspace and Airport Advisory Service at uncontrolled airports.

A pilot who does not keep abreast of and comply with the latest Regulations and procedures could be a source of danger to himself and to others in his vicinity. A Federal Aviation Administration report indicated that 549 "near mid-air" collisions were <u>reported</u> within the United States during one calendar year. This compared with 516 reports for the previous year. The Near Mid-Air Collision Report of 1968 listed 1,128 hazardous incidents. It would be reasonable to assume that other "near mid-air" collisions occurred that were not reported.

<u>Failure to comply with Regulations and Procedures increases the degree of potential mid-air collision hazards!</u>

Could any pilot with considerable flying experience truthfully say that he has never been involved in a "near miss" with other aircraft - or - that he is not seriously concerned about mid-air collisions? It is often so easy to fly for a long period of time with our head in the cockpit while we study charts or change radio frequencies.   Finally, something tells us that we should start looking around, and then we suddenly realize how foolish we were to expose ourselves to the potential hazards of a mid-air collision while we were preoccupied.

Most pilots know very well the danger of not properly guarding the airplane from other aircraft while their attention is divided between things inside and outside the cockpit -- yet is there a pilot flying today who will not some day break this rule of common sense?

TO AVOID OR REDUCE THE HAZARD OF TOO MUCH "EYES-INSIDE-THE-COCKPIT" FLYING, WHAT ACTION SHOULD A PILOT TAKE IN VFR CROSS-COUNTRY PREFLIGHT PLANNING?

(a) A pilot should obtain from the proper aeronautical charts all the information pertinent to the proposed route of flight. Information such as: headings, distances, checkpoints, altitudes, radio frequencies, etc., should be listed in a log format for easy reference. The reverse side of the FLIGHT PLAN (FAA Form 7233) provides a flight log for pilots.

(b) All necessary charts should be folded in proper sequence and conveniently located in the cockpit.

(c) The current issue of AIM — Basic Flight Information and ATC Procedures, should be reviewed before departure for information under such headings as: Good Operating Practices, Air Navigation Radio Aids, Airport-Air Navigation Lighting and Marking Aids, Weather, Preflight, Departure, Radar Assistance to VFR Aircraft, VFR Cruising Altitudes, Arrival, and Emergency Procedures.

(d) The appropriate Airport/Facility Directories should be consulted to obtain airport data and the proper sequence of radio frequencies for use at certain airports.

(e) An operational publication, that should be referred to before departing on the flight, is called the Graphic Notices and Supplemental Data. This publication contains a tabulation of Parachute Jump Areas, Special Notice Area Graphics, Terminal Area Graphics, Terminal Radar Service Area (TRSAs) Graphics, Olive Branch Routes, and other data.

(f) Another operational publication, called Notices to Airmen (NOTAMS), is essential to safety and should be consulted in preparation for the flight.

(g) A careful study of the aeronautical charts should be made to determine if your route of flight will traverse a Prohibited Area, Restricted Area, TCA, MOA, etc.

HOW DOES APPROACH CONTROL OR THE TOWER ASSIST IN PREVENTING MIDAIR COLLISIONS AT A CONTROLLED AIRPORT? Although it is always the direct responsibility of the pilot, when flying in VFR weather conditions, to avoid collision with other aircraft, information and clearances issued by the controllers are intended to aid pilots to the fullest extent in avoiding collisions. The controllers issue clearances that can be safely followed without collision hazard if reasonable caution is exercised by the pilot. By advising approach control or the tower of your position well in advance of entering the control zone (normally a minimum of 15 miles out), you will be able to receive information on other aircraft which might be in your vicinity as well as being assured of a safe and orderly entry into the traffic pattern.

☆ Note to Student Pilots: To receive additional assistance while operating in areas of concentrated air traffic, a student pilot should identify himself as a student pilot during the initial call to an FAA radio facility (Control Tower, FSS, Approach Control, etc.). For example: "Dayton Tower, this is Fleetwing 1234, Student Pilot, over."

WHY SHOULD A PILOT CHECK THE GRAPHIC NOTICES AND SUPPLEMENTAL DATA PUBLICATION? Before departing on an extensive cross-country flight in unfamiliar country, the pilot should check the Special Operations and Graphic Notices pertaining to: Parachute Jump Areas, Terminal Radar Service Areas, Terminal Area Graphic Notices, etc. By checking the data in this publication you may find it necessary to select an alternate route of flight to circumnavigate a particular area.

SAVE A FEW SECONDS OF EYES-INSIDE-THE-COCKPIT FLYING.

Before Takeoff —

- Tune the omnireceiver to the VOR frequency you intend to use after becoming airborne, and set the omnibearing selector to the desired radial.

- Determine which communication frequencies (Departure Control, FSS, etc.) you will use after departure and jot them down for quick reference. Attempting to unfold a sectional chart and search for an FSS frequency, in order to activate a flight plan, is not a safe practice while climbing to your enroute altitude.

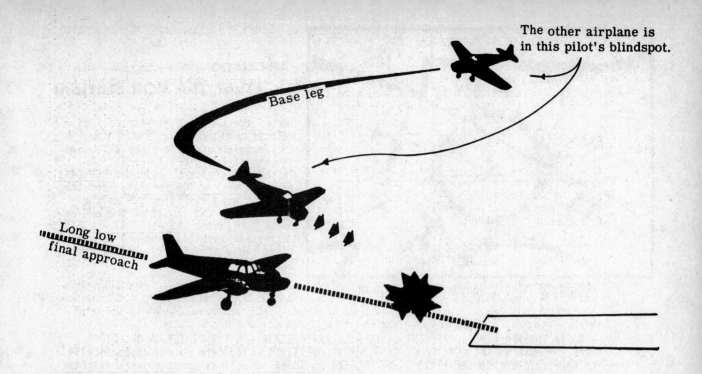

The collision that is about to happen as illustrated above can happen at any airport. A number of such accidents have already occurred - LOOK AROUND - DO NOT LET IT HAPPEN TO YOU.

IS TRAFFIC INFORMATION AVAILABLE AT CERTAIN NONCONTROLLED AIRPORTS? Yes, at certain noncontrolled airports (no control tower) where FAA Flight Service Stations are operating, there is available to you Airport Advisory Service. Use of this radio service will aid you in avoiding mid-air collisions.

WHAT SERVICE DOES THE AIRPORT ADVISORY SERVICE PROVIDE? The Flight Service Station (FSS) at uncontrolled airports provides airport advisory service to aircraft operating to or from the airport on which the station is located. The airport advisory service provides the following information to aircraft which are in communication with the station: Wind Direction and Velocity; Favored Runway; Altimeter Setting; Pertinent Known Traffic; Pertinent Known Field Conditions; Airport Taxi Routes and Traffic Patterns, etc.

NOTICE! There may be other aircraft in the vicinity of the airport not in communication with and thus not known by the FSS.

HOW DOES THE PILOT KNOW WHERE TO FIND AIRPORT ADVISORY SERVICE LOCATIONS? The locations are appropriately depicted on the Sectional Charts in this manner:

* * * * *

WHAT IS A SAFE WAY TO CLIMB OR DESCEND ON VICTOR AIRWAYS? The AIM Good Operating Practices section states: "During climb or descent, pilots are encouraged to fly to the right side of the center line of the radial forming the airway in order to avoid IFR and VFR cruising traffic operating along the center line of the airway."

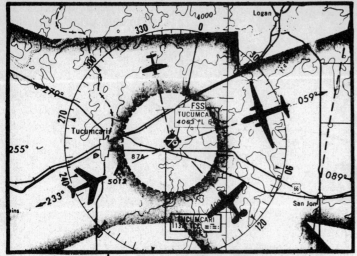

Possible Widely Scattered Aluminum

DESTINATION: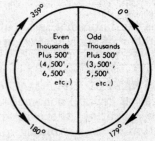
Over The VOR Station!

One of the FAA Near Mid-Air Collision Reports indicates that 81% of the incidents occurred in clear skies and unrestricted visibility conditions. Of the 549 incidents reported 255 (46%) occurred over a VOR facility, and the aircraft were utilizing VOR as the navigational aid in 89% of the en-route incidents. BE ALERT AT ALL TIMES: Unlimited visibility appears to encourage a sense of security which is not at all justified.

o o o

DOES ADHERING TO THE VFR ALTITUDE/FLIGHT LEVEL RULE APPROPRIATE FOR THE DIRECTION OF FLIGHT PLAY AN IMPORTANT ROLE IN THE ADVOIDANCE OF MID-AIR COLLISIONS? Yes, the rule is specifically designed to provide altitude separation, and applies to local as well as cross-country flights.

Many Airman Written Test applicants are incorrectly answering questions pertaining to the VFR Altitudes/Flight Levels rule for VFR cruising altitudes. When an aircraft is operated in VFR level cruising flight at more than 3,000 feet above the surface up to Flight Level 290 inclusive, the cruising alti- tudes (shown in the illustration to the right) shall be observed in accordance with the *magnetic course being flown. (Note: See Airman's Information Manual for more complete coverage of this subject.)

UNDER VFR-More than
3,000' ABOVE THE SURFACE

DO THE VFR CRUISING ALTITUDES APPLY BELOW 3000 FEET?
No, only when you are flying at more than 3,000 feet above the surface.

Assume that in the diagram below your flight traverses terrain with the approximate elevations as depicted. You desire to select a constant cruising altitude which will conform to VFR cruising altitude requirements and also have sufficient altitude above mountain peaks to avoid downdrafts or extreme turbulence. Altitudes above the surface in mountainous areas should be based on the lowest general terrain (excluding deep crevices or canyons).

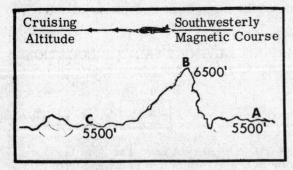

For example:
$$\begin{array}{r} 5500' \text{ general terrain elev.} \\ + 3000' \text{ above terrain} \\ \hline 8500' \text{ effective altitude} \end{array}$$

10,500' correct (even +500') at points A, B, C.
10,000' incorrect at points A, B, C.
9,500' incorrect at points A, B, C.
9,000' correct at point B-incorrect at points A, C.
8,500' correct (even +500') at points A, B, C.
8,000' correct at A, B, C.⎫ less than 3000' above
7,500' correct at A, B, C.⎬ surface but inadequate
7,000' correct at A, B, C.⎭ safety above peaks.

*NOTE - Magnetic course is true course corrected for variation. Do not confuse with: true course, compass course, magnetic heading, true heading or compass heading.

INTERPRETING SECTIONAL AERONAUTICAL CHARTS (SERIES 1)

This Exam-O-Gram concerns only the symbols associated with: (1) airports that are not served by a Control Tower or Flight Service Station, (2) obstruction and terrain elevation, and (3) appropriate checkpoints for VFR navigation.

Starting with 1977 editions of Sectional Aeronautical Charts a revised format was presented to include numerous changes in the use of symbols. Note the chart legend excerpt below.

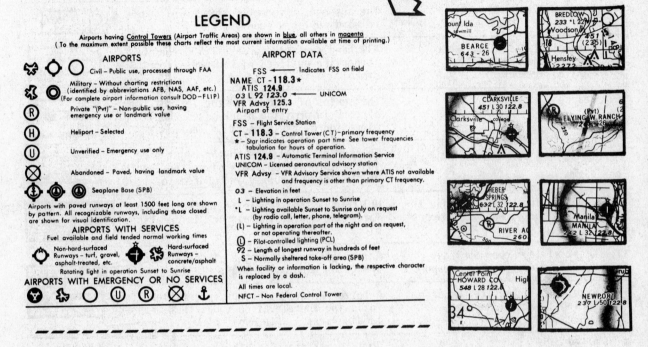

Refer to the airport symbols and the legend excerpt above to check your knowledge and understanding of these chart symbols. It is suggested that you answer each of the following questions to the best of your ability, then turn to page 2 to verify your answers.

1. Which airports have services for aircraft?

2. Which airports have emergency services only or no services at all?

3. Which airports have hard surfaced runways?

4. Which airports have no hard surfaced runways?

5. Which airports have hard surfaced runways at least 1,500 feet long?

6. Which airport is located at the highest elevation?

7. What is the elevation of this airport?

8. Which airport has the shortest landing area available?

9. What is the length of this landing area?

10. Which airports have UNICOM available?

11. Which airports have a rotating light?

12. Which airports have lighting facilities?

13. Which airport has lighting facilities available only upon prior request?

14. What is the length of the longest hard surfaced runway at the Newport Airport?

15. Which airports would be the easiest to find at night?

16. Which airports have hard surfaced runways but have no services, or at best, have only emergency services?

17. Which airport is restricted from public use?
How is an abandoned airport symbolized?

Q.	Answer	Explanation
1.	Clarksville, Heber Springs, Manila, Newport	Airport symbols with the projections indicate airports with services.
2.	Bearce, Bredlow, Flying W Ranch, Howard County	Those airport symbols without the projections indicate airports with emergency or no services. AIRPORTS WITH EMERGENCY OR NO SERVICES
3.	Bearce, Clarksville, Heber Springs, Howard County, Newport, Manila	Hard surfaced runways are outlined in the airport symbol.
4.	Bredlow, Flying W Ranch	The absence of runway outlines indicates no hard surfaced runways.
5.	Bearce, Clarksville, Heber Springs, Howard County, Manila, Newport	All hard surfaced runways 1,500 feet or longer are outlined within the airport symbol.
6.	Bearce	The series of numbers on the left of the airport information block gives the elevation of the airport in feet.
7.	643 feet	
8.	Bredlow	The series of numbers on the right side in the information block gives the length of the longest runway in <u>hundreds</u> of feet.
9.	2,200 feet	
10.	Clarksville, Heber Springs, Howard County, Manila, Newport	UNICOM availability is indicated at the far right end of the airport information block.
11.	Clarksville, Heber Springs, Howard County, Manila, Newport	A star at the top of the airport symbol indicates a rotating light.
12.	Bredlow, Clarksville, Heber Springs, Manila, Newport, Howard County	A letter L in the airport information line following the elevation indicates airport landing area lights available.
13.	Bredlow	An asterisk preceding the letter L indicates airport lighting only on prior request. Enclosing the letter L in parentheses indicates lights available part of the night and on request.
14.	5,000 feet	For those airports that have hard surfaced runways, the length given in the airport information line is that of the longest hard surfaced runway. However there is no symbol to indicate which one runway is the longest unless this can be determined by the relative lengths of the runway outlines.
15.	Clarksville, Heber Springs, Manila, Howard County, Newport	The rotating light would point them out.
16.	Bearce, Howard County	See answers and explanations to Q1 and Q3.
17.	Flying W Ranch	A letter R in the center of the airport symbol indicates the airport is restricted. Pvt in the airport information block indicates a private airport. An X indicates an abandoned airport.

Another area of difficulty in reading and interpreting sectional charts is determining obstruction and terrain elevation. It must be understood that the elevation of obstructions is referenced to both ground and sea level, while terrain and contour elevations are referenced to sea level. With reference to the two chart segments, how many of the following questions can you answer? Answers and explanations are given below.

1. What is the height, above sea level, of the group obstruction which is classed as higher than 1,000 feet above the ground (Fig. 1)?

2. What is the height, above ground level, of the single obstruction which is classed as an obstruction below 1,000 feet above ground level (Fig. 1)?

3. What is the meaning of the large numbers **29** in Figure 2?

4. At what elevation intervals are contour lines shown on sectional charts?

5. What is the highest value in feet printed on a contour line (Fig. 2)?

6. What is the significance of the contour lines being close together? Far apart?

7. What is the highest critical terrain elevation (Fig. 2)?

ANSWERS AND EXPLANATIONS TO QUESTIONS 1 THROUGH 7.

1. The tower shaped symbol 人 indicates the top of the obstruction is 1,000 feet or higher Above Ground Level. A double symbol 从 indicates a group obstruction. The height (top) above sea level of this obstruction in Fig 1 is 2,049 feet as shown in bold print and without parenthesis.

2. The inverted "V" shaped symbol ʌ denotes a single obstruction with the top less than 1,000 feet above ground level. The top of this obstruction is 306 feet AGL shown by the number in parenthesis below the bold faced number 686 representing the height MSL. A double symbol ʍ indicates a group obstruction.

FIG. 2

3. The large numbers **29** are called Maximum Elevation Figures (MEF). The Maximum Elevation Figures shown in quadrangles bounded by ticked lines of latitude and longitude are represented in THOUSANDS and HUNDREDS of feet above mean sea level. The MEF is based on information available concerning the highest known feature in each quadrangle, including terrain and obstructions (trees, towers, antennas, etc.).

   Example: 2,900 feet ------------------------**29**

   ☆ NOTE: This is an important change in the meaning of the large numbers on sectional charts issued after June 1977.

4. There are two intervals used; the basic contour interval which is 500 feet, and the intermediate contour interval which is 250 feet. Contour lines may extend for some distance before the elevation is indicated. Sometimes no elevation indication is found on the contour lines, but generally the elevation can be determined by comparing nearby contours.

5. The highest value printed is 2,000 feet. This is not the highest terrain in the area or on the chart. The highest terrain is determined by applying the appropriate interval to a labeled line. The colored coding for the particular chart which is found on the front of the chart must also be used to determine terrain elevation.

6. The closer the contour lines are together the steeper the slope of the terrain; the farther apart they are the more gradual the slope of the terrain.

7. The highest critical terrain elevation is 2,230 feet MSL. The specific point is indicated by a small black dot located near the number denoting the elevation.

Selecting Checkpoints For VFR Navigation

When flying the course shown above, which checkpoints indicated by arrows would be most appropriate for VFR navigation?   (Assuming a visibility greater than 10 miles.)

I	II	III
Batesville	Batesville	Courtland
Enid Reservoir	Courtland	Enid Reservoir
Water Valley (Town)	Taylor	Taylor
Oxford (Town)	Yocona River	Tula

Group I represents the best checkpoints since it includes only the prominent landmarks, i. e., larger towns and bodies of water.   Although the larger towns are not exactly on course, they are close enough to be easily identified.   Small towns and villages usually are poor checkpoints even though they lie right on course because they are difficult to identify.   Small towns may be important as checkpoints in sparsely populated areas, but care must be exercised or their use may be misleading.   Bodies of water reflect light and usually can be seen even with reduced visibility. Rivers are also excellent checkpoints, especially if they have prominent loops or bends, or are used in combination with other checkpoints.   In fact. using a combination of checkpoints is always an effective and desirable practice in pilotage.   Also, it should be noted that the highway to the left (north) of course provides an excellent reference for VFR navigation.

-4-

COMMON MISCONCEPTIONS (Series 2)

Each question in FAA Airman Written Examinations offers the examinee a group of four answers from which to select the answer he believes to be correct. Applicants' comments and analyses of the answer sheets indicate that particular incorrect answers are frequently being chosen because of a misconception regarding certain items of required aeronautical knowledge. This Exam-O-Gram, as well as Exam-O-Gram No. 17, attempts to correct a few of these preconceived ideas.

WHAT INDICATED AIRSPEED SHOULD BE USED FOR LANDING APPROACHES TO FIELDS OF HIGHER ELEVATIONS? For all practical purposes, use the SAME indication as you use at fields of lower elevations.

WILL THE SAME INDICATED APPROACH SPEED BE SAFE AT HIGH ELEVATIONS? YES, in relatively smooth air. We all know that as altitude increases, the air becomes less dense, and consequently with decreased drag the airplane travels faster through the air. However, this faster speed creates no increase in impact pressure on the airspeed pitot system because of the lesser air density. In other words, we get a higher True Airspeed with the same Indicated Airspeed. Although the True Airspeed (TAS) at which an airplane stalls in thinner air is higher, the margin of safety is unaffected since the airplane is actually flying at a higher True Airspeed. Nevertheless, for the purpose of maintaining positive control in unstable air, the use of a higher than normal indicated speed is recommended for approaches during the turbulent or gusty conditions prevalent in mountainous areas, just as is used at fields of lower elevations in these conditions.

WHAT EFFECT DOES THINNER AIR HAVE ON APPROACH AND LANDING? Even though using the same indicated airspeed that is appropriate for sea level operations, the True Airspeed is faster, resulting in a faster groundspeed (with a given wind condition). This increase in groundspeed naturally makes the landing distance longer and should be carefully considered when landing at high elevation fields, particularly if the field is short.

WHAT INDICATED AIRSPEED SHOULD BE USED ON TAKEOFF AT HIGH ELEVATIONS? Just as in landing, the groundspeed as well as the takeoff distance, will be greater at high elevation fields. However, don't let this mislead you into P-U-L-L-I-N-G the airplane off the ground. If you do, the airplane will mush and settle back to the ground in a stalled condition. Use the SAME indicated airspeed as you use for takeoff at fields with lower elevations.

WHAT WOULD YOU THINK IF YOU OVERHEARD THIS AIRPLANE "DISCREPANCY"
REPORT? "Hey, Chief, - fix this goofed-up airspeed indicator! I was practicing power-
off stalls with the gear and flaps down, but the airplane didn't stall until the pointer was
10 mph less than the white arc painted on the dial."

IS THE AIRSPEED INDICATOR FAULTY OR IS THE WHITE ARC MISPLACED? Not necessarily either one!
Remember, on some airplanes, the colored arcs on the airspeed dial mark the <u>Calibrated</u> Airspeed (CAS) and not merely the observed Indicated Airspeed (IAS) limitations.

> NOTE: The airspeed indicator markings may be either calibrated airspeed or Indi-
> cated airspeed, depending on the manufacturer and age of the airplane. Presently,
> several aircraft manufacturers are substituting indicated airspeed for calibrated
> airspeed markings. Refer to the Pilot's Operating Handbook for your aircraft.
> Some handbooks state: "IAS values published in the handbook assume zero instru-
> ment error."

WHAT IS CALIBRATED AIRSPEED (CAS), is Indicated Airspeed corrected for installation and
instrument error. A wide difference between these speeds may exist, particularly at low
airspeeds or under landing conditions. Installation error is caused when static atmosphere
in certain flight attitudes enters the static system with a different pressure than it does
in normal cruise conditions, creating a variance in pitot-static differential. Check the
airspeed correction data for each airplane. You may find (as in the typical table below)
that an IAS of 60 MPH is actually a CAS of 69 MPH.

AIRSPEED CORRECTION TABLE

FLAPS 0°								
IAS - MPH	60	80	100	120	140	160	180	200
CAS - MPH	69	82	100	119	139	160	181	202
*FLAPS 20°								
IAS - MPH	40	50	60	70	80	90	100	110
CAS - MPH	57	62	68	75	84	93	102	112
*FLAPS 40°								
IAS - MPH	40	50	60	70	80	90	100	110
CAS - MPH	57	62	68	75	83	92	102	111

*Maximum flap speed 110 MPH-CAS

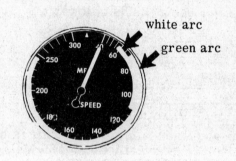

white arc
green arc

WHAT IS THE RELATIONSHIP BETWEEN AIRSPEED INDICATOR COLORED ARCS AND STALLING SPEEDS? In the
above illustrations, the white arc shows a stalling speed of 57 MPH (CAS), but because of
installation error (reflected in the table), this airplane may not stall with power-off and
gear and flaps down until the pointer is on 40 MPH (IAS). Similarly a variation is noted for
the green arc and stalling speed with gear and flaps UP. Since an airplane in flight is
operated most of the time within the upper speed range, installation error is normally
adjusted so as to be at a minimum in that range. This results in the greatest error at the
lower speed range, but provides a corresponding increase in the margin of safety at the
critical lower airspeeds.

* *

CAN NORMAL IN-FLIGHT ASSISTANCE BE RECEIVED FROM ALL VOR STATIONS? In the
NO, many VOR stations can be used <u>only</u> for navigation purposes. These stations
without voice capability have the navigation transmitting frequency underlined on the
newer aeronautical charts. Stations of this type <u>cannot</u> be used for weather information,
position reporting, flight plans, or emergency assistance.

IN TERMINAL FORECASTS DOES THE LETTER "C" MEAN CLEAR SKIES? No, — when used in the cloud group of the forecast, the letter "C" always identifies a forecast ceiling layer.

IS THE WIND ALWAYS SHOWN IN TERMINAL FORECASTS? NO, -- if the wind is forecast to be less than 10 knots, it is omitted.

IS THE VISIBILITY ALWAYS SHOWN IN TERMINAL FORECASTS? NO, -- if the visibility is forecast to be more than 6 miles, it is omitted.

IS THE HEIGHT OF CLOUD TOPS PREDICTED IN TERMINAL FORECASTS? NO, -- only the base of the clouds above the surface is predicted. Cloud tops are usually found in Pilot Reports (PIREPS), and often in Area Forecasts.

ARE TURBULENT CONDITIONS PREDICTED IN TERMINAL FORECASTS? NO, -- however, a prediction of gusty surface conditions may be included in the wind group of Terminal Forecasts.

* *

IN TELETYPE FORECASTS AND REPORTS, IS THE WIND INFORMATION RELATIVE TO TRUE NORTH OR MAGNETIC NORTH? All printed weather information, such as Area Forecasts, Terminal Forecasts, Aviation Weather Sequence Reports, Winds Aloft Forecasts, etc., presents the wind direction as measured from TRUE NORTH. To use this wind direction for the computations of problems in which magnetic values are required, magnetic variation should be applied. That is, add or subtract variation as appropriate to the area involved, when magnetic headings are desired.

IN RADIO BROADCASTS, IS THE WIND DIRECTION RELATIVE TO TRUE NORTH OR MAGNETIC NORTH? Surface wind direction given in traffic instructions by the tower, or in airport advisories by an FSS, is always given as MAGNETIC direction, so as to be readily related to the runway number which is also a magnetic direction. In weather broadcasts the wind is given in True direction for all reported stations except that of the station making the broadcast, in which case the wind is reported in Magnetic direction.

* *

CAN THE DATE AN ANNUAL INSPECTION IS DUE BE DETERMINED FROM AIRWORTHINESS CERTIFICATES? NO, -- with regard to the due date of an Annual Inspection, the Airworthiness Certificate is of no value unless it was issued within the preceding 12 calendar months. This certificate is issued only when the aircraft is certificated as being airworthy at the time of original manufacture (or after being substantially altered or repaired), and in most cases is issued only once in the lifetime of the aircraft.

FROM WHICH DOCUMENTS CAN THE DUE DATE OF AN ANNUAL INSPECTION BE DETERMINED? By checking the entries in the aircraft and engine maintenance records (in most cases aircraft and engine logbooks) certifying the latest Annual Inspection. If the records show the preceding inspection was performed on April 5, 1978, then the next inspection is due at the end of the 12th month subsequent to that date; that is, by the end of April 30, 1979.

IS THERE A DIFFERENCE BETWEEN AN AIRPORT TRAFFIC AREA AND A CONTROL ZONE? YES, definitely; although in some cases they may coincide laterally, in which case rules applicable to each are in effect.

WHAT IS AN AIRPORT TRAFFIC AREA? An Airport Traffic Area is the airspace surrounding an airport at which there is an <u>operating control tower</u>. It extends from the surface <u>upward to 3,000 feet,</u> and although not marked on the chart (except by the presence of control tower CT frequencies), it includes the area within a 5-mile radius from that airport (see Fig. 1). When operating <u>within</u> the Airport Traffic Area, a pilot is required, unless otherwise authorized, to maintain two-way radio communications with the tower. This does not apply when operating for the purpose of taking off or landing at airports without a control tower that happen to be within the Airport Traffic Area of another airport. This rule is also not applicable when the tower is <u>not</u> in operation nor at airports without control towers <u>outside</u> of an Airport Traffic Area. (See Fig. 2.) The airport traffic <u>pattern</u> of an airport is not to be confused with an Airport Traffic <u>Area.</u>

Airport Traffic Area

(Tower Frequency)

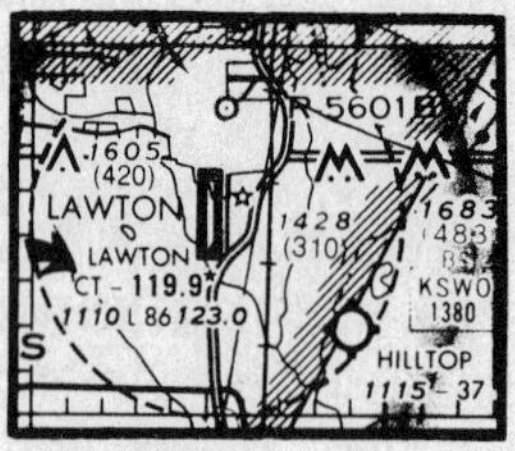

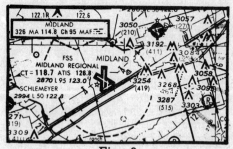

Fig. 1

No Airport Traffic Area →

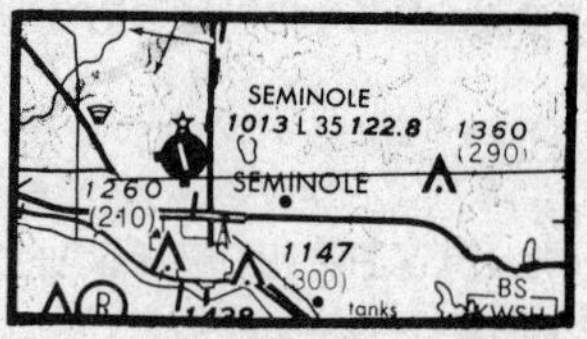

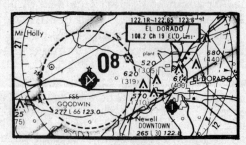

Fig. 2

WHAT IS A CONTROL ZONE? A Control Zone is an airspace surrounding one or more airports, within which, rules additional to those governing flight in control areas and "airport traffic areas," apply for the protection of air traffic. Normally, an aircraft shall not be operated under Visual Flight Rules within a Control Zone <u>beneath a ceiling of less than 1,000 feet or with a visibility of less than 3 miles.</u> To do so requires a <u>special VFR clearance from Air Traffic Control.</u> If the airport lies within a Control Zone as well as an Airport Traffic Area (see Fig. 3), this clearance is obtained through the control tower. However, <u>all Control Zones do not have a control tower</u> or lie within an Airport Traffic Area (see Fig. 4). In this case arriving and departing traffic is controlled by ATC either by direct communication between the control center and the pilot, or through an appropriate radio facility. Frequently, clearances are conveyed to an aircraft by a nearby Flight Service Station (FSS). All Control Zones are marked on charts by a circular broken line, normally a 5-mile radius with extensions as necessary for IFR approaches, extending from the <u>surface upward</u> to the Continental Control Area, and may encompass more than one airport. These special rules are also applicable to the other airports within the Control Zone boundaries.

Fig. 3

Fig. 4

THE EFFECT OF WIND ON AN AIRPLANE

While acquiring aeronautical knowledge, we sometimes neglect, or do not thoroughly understand some of the fundamental principles involved in flying an airplane. One of the basic facts of flight which is involved in the safety of almost every flight, and yet in FAA Airman Written Examinations seems to be one of the least understood is THE RELATIONSHIP BETWEEN THE AIRPLANE AND THE AIR SURROUNDING IT.

DOES WIND AFFECT THE AIRPLANE'S AIRSPEED? With the possible exception of wind shear, severe gusts, sudden lulls, etc., NO. Remember, the airspeed is the speed at which the airplane is traveling through the air. Even though the air mass might also be moving (wind), the relationship of the airplane's movement to the mass of air remains unchanged. This may be explained by assuming a person is walking forward at 5 mph inside a railroad train which is traveling 60 mph. Regardless of the train's speed, the person is walking 5 mph in relation to the train. If the person turns around and walks toward the rear of the train, or if the train slows to a stop, he is still walking 5 mph in relation to the train. Similarly, the direction and speed of the movement of the air mass (wind) through which the airplane flies, has no effect on its speed through the air (airspeed). It follows then that stalling speed is also unaffected by a steady normal wind (Exam-O-Gram #17).

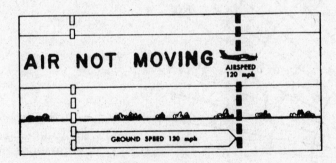

Figure 1

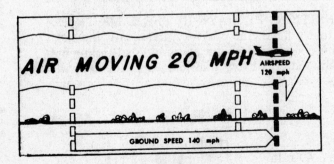

Figure 2

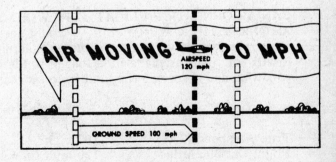

Figure 3

*Exam-O-Grams are non-directive in nature and are
issued solely as an information service to individuals
interested in Airman Written Examinations.

DOES WIND AFFECT THE AIRPLANE'S GROUNDSPEED? Definitely yes! Again consider the case of a person walking inside a railroad train. Since the train is moving 60 mph in relation to the ground and the person is walking forward 5 mph in relation to the train, he is actually traveling 65 mph in relation to the ground (groundspeed). Conversely, if he walks toward the rear of the train at a rate of 5 mph and the train is moving 60 mph, he is actually traveling at a rate of 55 mph in relation to the ground. Similarly, an airplane flying at an airspeed of 120 mph with a tailwind of 20 mph is traveling at a groundspeed of 140 mph (Figure 2). After turning around so the wind is now a headwind of 20 mph, the airplane would be traveling 100 mph in relation to the ground, or with a 40 mph reduction in groundspeed (Figure 3). Since groundspeed is not a factor in stalling speed, the airplane is no closer to a stall flying into the wind than flying with the wind.

IS THE GROUNDSPEED CHANGED BY AN AMOUNT EQUAL TO THE WINDSPEED? Not always! The groundspeed is increased or decreased by the full amount of the windspeed only when a direct headwind or direct tailwind exists. As the angle between the nose of the airplane and the wind direction increases (up to approximately 90° on either side) the headwind component decreases, resulting in a gradual reduction in the effect of wind on the airplane's groundspeed (see Figure 4). As the angle increases from approximately a 90° crosswind to 180°, the tailwind component increases with a corresponding increase in groundspeed.

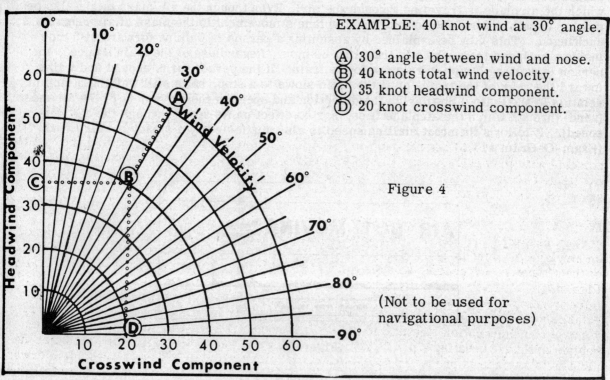

EXAMPLE: 40 knot wind at 30° angle.

Ⓐ 30° angle between wind and nose.
Ⓑ 40 knots total wind velocity.
Ⓒ 35 knot headwind component.
Ⓓ 20 knot crosswind component.

Figure 4

(Not to be used for navigational purposes)

CAN A ROUND-TRIP FLIGHT WITH WIND CONDITIONS BE MADE IN THE SAME TIME AS ONE WITH NO WIND? No! It would seem that a headwind one way and a tailwind the other way would average the same as making the round-trip under no wind conditions, but it will not. The airplane flies longer in the headwind condition than it does in the tailwind condition and therefore the total time increases.

	20 mph Wind	No Wind
True Airspeed (TAS)	100 mph	100 mph
Flight Out 200 Miles	120 mph GS = 1 hr. 40 min.	100 mph GS = 2 hrs.
Flight Back 200 Miles	80 mph GS = 2 hr. 30 min.	100 mph GS = 2 hrs.
Total Time	4 hr. 10 min.	4 hrs.
Average GS	96 mph	100 mph

DOES AN AIRPLANE IN FLIGHT TRAVEL IN THE DIRECTION IT IS HEADED? Not always! The airplane moves forward because of engine thrust pulling in the direction it is headed. However, if the mass of air surrounding the airplane is also moving (wind) the airplane, in addition to its forward movement, is carried in the same direction and at the same speed as the air mass. Thus, we have two directional forces acting on the airplane--the thrust component and the wind component. If the thrust is moving the airplane forward toward the east and the wind is moving it sideward toward the south, then the resultant path over the ground will be east-southeasterly. (See Figure 5.) This sideward movement of the airplane caused by the wind is called "drift."

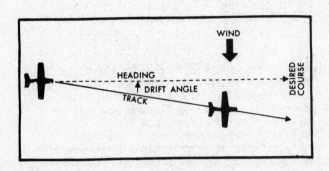

Figure 5

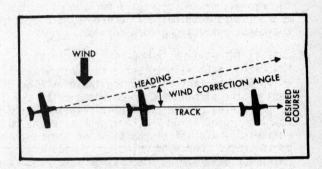

Figure 6

HOW CAN WE COMPENSATE FOR DRIFT IN ORDER TO MAKE GOOD A DESIRED COURSE OVER THE GROUND? We must head the airplane into the wind at an angle at which the direction of the thrust component will compensate for the wind component. This correction angle or "crab" should be sufficient to make the resultant path over the ground (ground track) coincide with the desired course over the ground. (See Figure 6.) The necessary heading can be determined by trial and error, or by wind triangle computations based on true airspeed, true course, and wind direction and speed.

DOES WIND AFFECT AN AIRPLANE ON THE GROUND THE SAME AS IN THE AIR? In certain respects, no! In addition to being moved forward through the air by its own power, an airplane in flight is carried in the same direction and at the same speed as the movement of the air mass surrounding it. Since it is free to move with the air mass, the airplane in flight does not "feel" this movement of the mass of air (except when wind-shear, or sudden lulls or gusts are encountered). Therefore, after the proper correction for drift is established, control pressure need not be maintained for directional control. However, during ground operation, the friction of the airplane's wheels in contact with the ground resists drifting, creating a pivot point at the main wheels. Since a greater portion of the airplane's surface is presented to the crosswind aft of the wheels than is presented forward of the wheels, the airplane tends to "weathervane" or turn into any crosswind. In this case corrective control pressures must be applied and maintained for directional control on the ground. This weathervaning occurs even in tricycle (nose wheel) gear airplanes, unless the wheels are located well aft in relation to the side surface of the airplane.

Figure 7

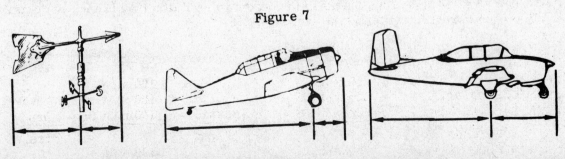

WHAT EFFECT DO CROSSWINDS HAVE ON TAKEOFF AND LANDING? While the airplane is free of the ground, the wind has the same effect as explained in preceding paragraphs for an airplane in flight. However, on takeoff and landings, an airplane should never be allowed to contact the ground while <u>drifting</u> or while <u>headed in a direction other than that in which it is moving over the ground.</u> Unless proper action is taken to prevent this from occurring, severe side stresses will be imposed on the landing gear, and a sudden swerve or ground loop may occur. When this develops, we have an almost uncontrollable situation and consequently, <u>a serious accident potential</u>.

CAN TAKEOFFS AND LANDINGS BE SAFELY MADE IN ALL CROSSWIND CONDITIONS? Not always! Takeoffs and landings in certain crosswind conditions are inadvisable or even dangerous. If the crosswind is great enough to warrant an extreme drift correction, a hazardous landing condition may result. Therefore, always consider the takeoff or landing capabilities with respect to the reported surface wind conditions and the available landing directions. The <u>absence</u> of proper crosswind techniques, or the <u>disregard</u> for adequate consideration of the airplane's characteristics and capabilities with respect to crosswind conditions, are reflected by the continual rise in accidents involving ground control.

WHAT IS THE MAXIMUM SAFE CROSSWIND CONDITION? Before an airplane is <u>type certificated</u> by the FAA, it must be flight tested to meet certain requirements. Among these is the demonstration of being satisfactorily controllable with no exceptional degree of skill or alertness on the part of the pilot in 90° crosswinds up to a velocity equal to 0.2 V_{SO}. This means a windspeed of two-tenths of the airplane's stalling speed with power off and gear and flaps down. (If the stalling speed is 60 MPH, then the airplane must be capable of being landed in a 12 MPH 90° crosswind.) To inform the pilot of the airplane's capability, Regulations require that the demonstrated crosswind velocity be made available. Certain Airplane Owner's Manuals provide a chart for determining the maximum safe wind velocities for various degrees of crosswind for that particular airplane.

FACTORS AFFECTING STALL SPEED

A recent report indicates that approximately 80% of all accidents are pilot caused. The major cause of <u>fatal</u> accidents is listed as "failed to maintain airspeed (or flying speed) resulting in a stall." Although many of these stalls may have occurred under the stress and duress of other problems such as <u>disorientation</u> during limited visibility or at night, <u>improper division of attention</u>, etc., a review of statistical analyses of written examinations indicates a lack of knowledge and understanding of the various factors that can cause or contribute to a stall. This Exam-O-Gram discusses some of the more important, ever-present factors of which the pilot must have an understanding so that he will instinctively avoid or compensate for situations, conditions, and attitudes which may lead to a stall--even under the stress and duress of additional problems he may encounter in flight.

WHAT CAUSES AN AIRPLANE TO STALL? All stalls are caused by exceeding the critical angle of attack. Knowing this particular fact does not necessarily help the pilot. What is more important to the pilot is to know what factors are likely to contribute to or cause this angle of attack to be exceeded.

IS IT NECESSARY FOR THE AIRPLANE TO HAVE A RELATIVELY LOW AIRSPEED IN ORDER FOR IT TO STALL? No! An airplane can be stalled <u>at any airspeed</u>. All that is necessary is to exceed the critical angle of attack. This can be done at any airspeed if the pilot applies abrupt or excessive back pressure on the elevator control. A stall that occurs at a relatively high speed is referred to as an accelerated or high speed stall.

FIG. 1

IS IT NECESSARY FOR THE AIRPLANE TO HAVE A RELATIVELY HIGH PITCH ATTITUDE IN ORDER FOR IT TO STALL? No! An airplane can be stalled <u>in any attitude.</u> Repeating again the statement made above - all that is necessary is to exceed the critical angle of attack. This can occur in any attitude by application of abrupt or excessive back pressure on the elevator control.

DOES WEIGHT AFFECT THE STALLING SPEED? Yes! As the weight of the airplane is increased, the stall speed increases. Due to the greater weight, a higher angle of attack must be maintained to produce the additional lift to support the additional weight in flight. Therefore, the critical angle of attack will be reached at a higher airspeed when loaded to maximum gross weight than when flying solo with no baggage.

DOES THE CENTER-OF-GRAVITY LOCATION (WEIGHT DISTRIBUTION) AFFECT STALL SPEED? Yes! The farther forward the center of gravity, the higher the stalling speed. The farther aft the center of gravity, the lower the stalling speed.

DOES THIS MEAN THAT THE WEIGHT SHOULD BE DISTRIBUTED IN THE AIRPLANE SO THAT THE CG IS AS FAR TO THE REAR AS POSSIBLE? No! This may present problems with stability that will far outweigh any advantages obtained by the decrease in stall speed.

DO FLAPS AFFECT STALLING SPEED? Yes! The use of flaps reduces stalling speed. The Stall Speed Chart (Figure 2) excerpted from an airplane flight manual illustrates this fact. This also can be readily verified by checking the color coding on any airspeed indicator. The lower airspeed limit of the white arc (power-off stalling speed with gear and flaps in the landing configuration) is less than the lower airspeed limit of the green arc (power-off stalling speed in the clean configuration).

This fact is important to the pilot in that when making no-flap landings, a higher indicated airspeed should be maintained than when landing with flaps. The manufacturers' recommendations should be adhered to as to approach speeds with various configurations.

STALL SPEED, POWER OFF

Gross Weight 3000 lbs. CONFIGURATION	ANGLE OF BANK			
	0°	20°	40°	60°
GEAR & FLAPS UP	65	67	74	92
GEAR DOWN, FLAPS 20°	61	63	70	86
GEAR DOWN, FLAPS 40°	60	62	69	85

SPEEDS ARE MPH, TIAS

FIG. 2. (Note: TIAS identical with CAS)

DOES AN ACCUMULATION OF FROST, SNOW, OR ICE ON THE WINGS AFFECT STALLING SPEED? Yes! Even a light accumulation of frost, snow, or ice on the wings can cause a significant increase in stalling speed. It can increase it so much that the airplane is unable to take off. The accumulation disrupts the smooth flow of air over the wing thus decreasing the lift it produces. To make up for the lost lift, a higher angle of attack must be used or a higher speed must be attained on the takeoff roll. The runway may not be long enough to attain the necessary speed and even though the airplane may become airborne, it could be so close to the stall speed that it would not be possible to maintain flight once the airplane climbs above the comparatively shallow zone where ground effect prevails. DO NOT TAKE OFF UNTIL ALL FROST, SNOW, OR ICE HAS MELTED OR BEEN REMOVED FROM THE AIRPLANE.

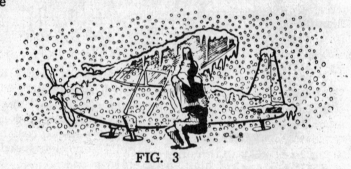

FIG. 3

DOES AN INCREASE IN ALTITUDE AFFECT THE INDICATED AIRSPEED AT WHICH AN AIRPLANE STALLS? An increase in altitude has no effect on the indicated airspeed at which an airplane stalls at altitudes normally used by general aviation aircraft. That is, for all practical purposes, the indicated stalling speed remains the same regardless of altitude in this range. This fact is important to the pilot in that the same indicated airspeed should be maintained during the landing approach regardless of the elevation or the density altitude at the airport of landing. (Follow the manufacturer's recommendations in this regard.) If higher than normal approach airspeed is used, a longer landing distance will be required.

DOES AN INCREASE IN ALTITUDE AFFECT THE TRUE AIRSPEED AT WHICH AN AIRPLANE STALLS? Since true airspeed normally increases as altitude increases (for a given indicated airspeed), then true airspeed at which an airplane stalls generally increases with an increase in altitude. Under non-standard conditions (temperature warmer than standard) there is an additional increase in true airspeed above the indicated airspeed.

OF WHAT SIGNIFICANCE IS THIS TO THE PILOT? It is significant in that when landing at higher elevations or under higher density altitudes, he is operating at higher true airspeeds (and therefore higher groundspeeds) throughout the approach, touchdown, and landing roll. This results in a greater distance to clear obstacles during the approach, a longer ground roll, and consequently, the need for a longer runway. If, in addition, the pilot is operating under the misconception that a higher than normal indicated airspeed should be used under these conditions, the situation is further compounded due to the additional increase in groundspeed. (See EXAM-O-GRAM No. 26.)

DOES TURBULENCE AFFECT STALLING SPEED? Yes! Turbulence can cause a large increase in stalling speed. Encountering an upward vertical gust causes an abrupt change in relative wind. This results in an equally abrupt increase in angle of attack which could result in a stall. This fact is important to the pilot in that when making an approach under turbulent conditions, a higher than normal approach speed should be maintained. Also, in moderate or greater turbulence, an airplane should not be flown above maneuvering speed.

At the same time, it should not be flown too far below maneuvering speed since a sudden severe vertical gust may cause an inadvertent stall due to the higher angle of attack at which it will already be flying.

DOES ANGLE OF BANK AFFECT STALLING SPEED? Yes! As the angle of bank increases in a constant altitude turn, the stalling speed increases. This is easily seen from the STALL SPEED CHARTS (Figs. 2 and 4) which show the increase in stall speed as the angle of bank increases--Fig. 4 in terms of percent, Fig. 2 the actual values for one airplane. At a 60° bank stalling speed is 40% greater than in straight-and-level flight (25-27 mph for the specific example.) At angles of bank above 60°, stall speed increases very rapidly, and at approximately 75° it is doubled with respect to straight-and-level stall speed (Fig. 4).

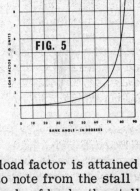

DOES LOAD FACTOR AFFECT STALLING SPEED? Yes! As the load factor increases, stalling speed increases. When the load factor is high, stalling speed is high. A comparison of the two charts (Figs. 4 and 5) should easily show this relationship. Load factor is the ratio of the load supported by the wings to the actual weight of the airplane and its contents. At a load factor of 2, the wings support twice the weight of the airplane; at a load factor of 4, they support four times the weight of the airplane. Normal category airplanes with a maximum gross weight of less than 4,000 pounds are required to have a minimum limit load factor of 3.8. (The limit load factor is that load factor an airplane can sustain without taking a permanent set in the structure.) Note from the load factor chart (Fig. 5) that this minimum limit load factor is attained in a constant altitude turn at a bank of approximately 75°. Also note from the stall speed chart (Fig. 4) that at this angle of bank, the stall speed is twice as great as in straight-and-level flight. There are two reasons then why excessively steep banks should be avoided--an airplane will stall at a much higher airspeed and the limit load factor can be exceeded. The danger can be compounded when the nose gets down in a steep turn if the pilot attempts to raise it to the level flight attitude without shallowing the bank since the load factor may be increased even more. This is the situation as it generally exists when, due to disorientation, the pilot enters a diving spiral (often referred to as the "graveyard spiral") and attempts to recover with elevator pressure alone.

- 3 -

WHAT FACTORS CAUSE AN INCREASE IN LOAD FACTOR? Any maneuvering of the airplane that produces an increase in centrifugal force will cause an increase in load factor. Turning the airplane or pulling out of a dive are examples of maneuvering that will increase the centrifugal force and thus produce an increase in load factor. When you have a combination of turning and pulling out of a dive, such as recovering from a diving spiral, you are, in effect, placing yourself in double jeopardy. This is why you must avoid highspeed diving spirals or if you accidentally get into one--be careful how you recover. Turbulence can also produce large load factors. This is why an airplane should be slowed to maneuvering speed or below when encountering moderate or greater turbulence.

CAN THE PILOT RECOGNIZE WHEN THERE IS AN INCREASE IN LOAD FACTOR? Yes! He can recognize it by the feeling of increased body weight or the feeling that he is being forced down into the seat-- the greater the load factor the greater this feeling of increased weight or of being forced down in the seat (Figs. 6 and 7). It is the same feeling one has when riding the roller coaster at the bottom of a dip or going around a banked curve. This feeling of increased body weight is important to the pilot because it should, if it becomes excessive, have the immediate effect of a red flag being waved in his face to warn him that the airplane will now stall at a higher airspeed or that the limit load factor can be exceeded, resulting in structural failure.

FIG. 6

DOES SPEED AFFECT LOAD FACTOR? Speed does not, in itself, affect load factor. However, it has a pronounced effect on how much of an increase in load factor can be produced by strong vertical gusts, or by the pilot through abrupt or excessive application of back pressure on the elevator control. This is why airspeed should be reduced to maneuvering speed or below if moderate or greater turbulence is encountered. At maneuvering speed or below, the airplane is stressed to handle any vertical gust that normally will be encountered. Also, below this speed, the pilot can make abrupt full deflection of the elevator control and not exceed the maximum load factor for which the airplane is stressed. However, it should be noted that the reason this is possible is because the airplane will stall, thus relieving the load factor. At airspeeds above maneuvering speed, abrupt full deflection of the elevator control or strong vertical gusts can cause the limit load factor to be exceeded. As airspeed continues to increase above maneuvering speed, the limit load factor can be exceeded with less and less turbulence or abrupt use or deflection of the controls.

WHAT IS THE RELATIONSHIP BETWEEN A HIGH SPEED (ACCELERATED) STALL AND LOAD FACTOR? The higher the airspeed when an airplane is stalled, the greater the load factor. When an airplane stalls at a slow airspeed, the load factor will be very little more than one. When stalled at an airspeed twice as great as the normal stall speed, the limit load factor for normal category airplanes probably will be exceeded. This fact can be determined from the stall speed (Fig. 4) and load factor (Fig. 5) charts. See also discussion of "Does Load Factor Affect Stalling Speed" (page 3).

FIG. 7

USE OF PERFORMANCE CHARTS

A report of an accident was stated in the following words: "Takeoff was attempted on a 1,600-foot strip; the airplane cleared the fences but sank back and struck a ditch." The pilot stated that he failed to consider the effects of the grassy, rough field, the 90° temperature, heavy load of fuel and passengers, and the calm wind. COULD THE USE OF THE TAKEOFF PERFORMANCE CHART FOR HIS AIRCRAFT HAVE PREDICTED THE SAD ENDING TO THIS FLIGHT?

WHAT ARE PERFORMANCE CHARTS? They are charts that describe or predict the performance of an aircraft under a given set of conditions or ground rules. They may be in tabular or graph form. (Because of their importance to safety, all applicants are being tested, and will continue to be tested, on use of performance charts in the written examinations.)

WHERE DO YOU FIND PERFORMANCE CHARTS? You can find them in the FAA-approved Airplane Flight Manual and the Owner's Manual or Handbook prepared by the manufacturer. In many cases, the FAA-approved Flight Manual must be carried in the aircraft at all times.

ARE THE CONDITIONS OR GROUND RULES UNDER WHICH YOU USE A PARTICULAR TYPE PERFORMANCE CHART ALWAYS THE SAME? No. The particular set of conditions or ground rules, as well as format, will vary with the manufacturer. Although ground rules for their use may be different, the information obtainable is essentially the same--takeoff and landing distance (ground run or roll and to clear a 50-foot obstacle), fuel consumption, rate of climb, true airspeed, etc.

HOW ACCURATE SHOULD YOU CONSIDER THE PREDICTIONS OF PERFORMANCE CHARTS? You will be headed in the safe direction if you always consider the performance of the airplane you fly to be less than predicted by the performance charts. The following statement is contained in one airplane flight manual: "Flight tests from which the performance data was obtained were flown with a new, clean airplane, correctly rigged and loaded, and with an engine capable of delivering its full rated power." You can expect to do as well only if your airplane, too, is kept in the peak of condition.

IS IT NECESSARY THAT YOU ALWAYS CONSULT PERFORMANCE CHARTS PRIOR TO TAKEOFF OR LANDING? No. Obviously, if you are taking off or landing on a 10,000-foot runway in a light airplane, you need not check the takeoff or landing data charts. But where is the dividing line-- 6,000? 4,000? 2,000? This depends on a lot of factors which include the equipment you are flying; pilot skill, proficiency, and familiarity with equipment; and the relative values of the 3 major factors affecting aircraft performance (density altitude, gross weight, and wind) plus the type and condition of the runway.

WHEN SHOULD YOU CHECK YOUR PERFORMANCE CHARTS? Any time there is doubt in your own mind, whether it be due to the length and/or condition of the runway, the high density altitude, a recognition of your own limitations or a lack of familiarity with the equipment you are flying--which will be alleviated through the use of performance charts. You should begin an operation with complete confidence in its success. Use everything at your disposal to establish this confidence. Charts do not cover all conditions that might have an effect on performance, but by making adequate allowances to the information obtained, you can ensure a greater margin of safety.

WHAT CAN YOU OBTAIN FROM TAKEOFF PERFORMANCE CHARTS? You can find the predicted length of the takeoff ground run and/or the predicted distance necessary to clear a 50-foot obstacle (which includes the ground roll). For example:

Chart 1: At an elevation of 4,000 feet, zero mph wind, 75° F, 15° of flaps, and maximum gross weight (2,300 lbs. for this airplane) the predicted ground run is 1,380 feet and the predicted distance necessary to clear a 50-foot obstacle is 2,065 feet. If the airplane weighed 200 lbs. less than maximum gross weight, these distances would be reduced by 30% and become 966 feet and 1,445 feet, respectively. (See NOTE at bottom of chart.)

OBSTACLE TAKE-OFF DATA   15° FLAPS

Wind Vel. mph	Sea Level			2000 Ft.			4000 Ft.			6000 Ft.			8000 Ft.		
	Temp. °F	Ground Run Ft.	To Clear 50' Obst. Ft.	Temp. °F	Ground Run Ft.	To Clear 50' Obst. Ft.	Temp. °F	Ground Run Ft.	To Clear 50' Obst. Ft.	Temp. °F	Ground Run Ft.	To Clear 50' Obst. Ft.	Temp. °F	Ground Run Ft.	To Clear 50' Obst. Ft.
0	30	785	1175	20	900	1310	15	1060	1580	10	1260	1895	0	1175	2305
	59	890	1320	52	1035	1525	45	1215	1810	38	1430	2170	30	1695	2735
	90	1005	1490	80	1160	1720	75	1380	2065	70	1610	2560	60	1890	3275
10	30	620	955	20	715	1095	15	850	1300	10	1015	1570	0	1195	1920
	59	705	1080	52	830	1260	45	975	1495	38	1160	1810	30	1380	2290
	90	805	1220	80	935	1425	75	1110	1715	70	1335	2135	60	1575	2780

CHART 1   NOTE: Decrease distance approximately 15% for 100 pounds decrease in gross weight.

Chart 2: At an elevation of 4,000 ft., 75° F, flaps up, and gross weight of 2,800 lbs., the takeoff distance is 1,600 ft. If you get 1,275 ft., it is because you used the same set of ground rules that you used in Chart 1. Since Chart 2 is based on standard altitude (standard temperature and pressure), you must first convert the elevation (to be completely accurate, the pressure altitude at that elevation) and temperature to a density altitude. A temperature of 75° F at an elevation (pressure altitude) of 4,000 ft. results in a density altitude of approximately 6,000 ft. (see Density Altitude Chart, page 4). Using an altitude of 6,000 ft. in Chart 2, you obtain the predicted takeoff distance of 1,600 ft. (75° F = 24° C)

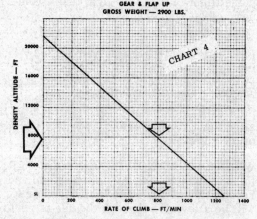

WHAT CAN YOU OBTAIN FROM CLIMB PERFORMANCE CHARTS? Primarily, the rate of climb under various conditions. The information from these charts becomes exceedingly important when you have to cross high mountain ranges relatively soon after takeoff. Some charts also give the best climb airspeed and fuel consumed during the climb. For example:

CLIMB DATA

GROSS WEIGHT LBS.	AT SEA LEVEL & 59°F.			AT 5000 FT. & 41°F.			AT 10000 FT. & 23°F.		
	BEST CLIMB IAS MPH	RATE OF CLIMB FT/MIN	GAL. OF FUEL USED	BEST CLIMB IAS MPH	RATE OF CLIMB FT/MIN	From SL FUEL USED	BEST CLIMB IAS MPH	RATE OF CLIMB FT/MIN	From SL FUEL USED
2100	87	1470	1.5	82	1200	2.8	78	925	4.3
2400	88	1210	1.5	84	960	3.1	80	710	5.0
2650	90	1030	1.5	86	795	3.5	83	560	5.9

Note: Flaps up, full throttle and 2600 RPM. Mixture leaned for smooth operation above 5000 ft. Fuel used includes warm-up and take-off allowance.

Chart 3

Chart 3: At 5,000 ft., 41° F, and 2,100 lbs. gross weight, the rate of climb is 1,200 ft./min.; best climb speed is 82 mph; and fuel used to climb from sea level to 5,000 ft. is 2.8 gal. At a gross weight of 2,650 lbs. under the same conditions, the rate of climb is 795 ft./min.

GEAR & FLAP UP
GROSS WEIGHT — 2900 LBS.

CHART 4

DENSITY ALTITUDE — FT

RATE OF CLIMB — FT/MIN

Chart 4: At 5,000 ft., 86° F, and 2,900 lbs. gross weight, the rate of climb is approximately 810 ft. -- not 970 ft. Note that you must first convert the altitude and temperature to a density altitude using the Density Altitude Chart, page 4. The density altitude at this altitude and temperature is approximately 7,750 ft. (86° F = 30° C)

WHAT CAN YOU OBTAIN FROM CRUISE PERFORMANCE CHARTS? Some of the items you can obtain include recommended power settings at various altitudes, along with percent of brake horsepower at these settings, rate of fuel consumption (gal/hr), true airspeed, hours of endurance with full tanks, and range in miles under standard conditions and zero wind. Not all of these values are obtainable from all charts. For example:

Chart 5: At 5,000 ft., 2,300 RPM, and 21 inches of manifold pressure, you should get 64% rated power, approximately 151 mph true airspeed, and consume approximately 11.9 gal./hr. of fuel which will give you an endurance of 4.6 hrs. and a range of 700 miles under standard conditions, zero wind, and full fuel tanks.

CRUISE AND RANGE PERFORMANCE

Altitude	RPM	M.P.	BHP	%BHP	TAS MPH	Gal./Hr.	End. Hours	Mi/Gal.	Range Miles
5000	2450	23	179	78	163	14.5	3.8	11.2	615
		22	169	73	159	13.6	4.0	11.7	640
		21	161	70	156	13.0	4.2	12.0	660
		20	150	65	151	12.2	4.5	12.5	685
	2300	23	167	73	158	13.4	4.1	11.8	650
		22	158	69	155	12.6	4.4	12.2	675
		21	148	64	151	11.9	4.6	12.7	700
		20	139	60	146	11.2	4.9	13.1	720
	2200	23	157	68	155	12.4	4.4	12.5	685
		22	148	64	151	11.7	4.7	12.9	710
		21	138	60	146	11.0	5.0	13.3	730
		20	131	57	143	10.5	5.2	13.6	750

Cruise performance shown is based on standard conditions, zero wind, lean mixture, 55 gallons of fuel, no fuel reserve, and 2650 pounds gross weight.

Chart 5

Chart 6: At 8,000 ft. you can obtain 55% rated power and 10.3 gal./hr. fuel consumption with 2,200 RPM and 19 inches of manifold pressure.

CRUISE PERFORMANCE

ALT.	RPM	% BHP	TAS MPH	58.8 Gal Endurance Hours	58.8 Gal Range Miles
2500	2500	75	130	6.0	773
	2350	63	118	7.1	832
	2200	53	107	8.4	894
3500	2525	75	131	6.0	775
	2400	65	121	6.9	827
	2250	55	110	8.0	874
4500	2550	75	132	6.0	780
	2400	63	120	7.0	841
	2250	53	109	8.3	905
5500	2600	77	135	5.8	775
	2450	65	123	6.8	837
	2300	55	112	8.0	887

CHART 7

Power Setting Table —

Press. Alt. 1000 Feet	Std. Alt. Temp. °F	138 HP — 55% Rated Approx. Fuel 10.3 Gal./Hr. RPM AND MAN. PRESS.				163 HP — 65% Rated Approx. Fuel 12.3 Gal./Hr. RPM AND MAN. PRESS.			
		2100	2200	2300	2400	2100	2200	2300	2400
SL	59	21.6	20.8	20.2	19.6	24.2	23.3	22.6	22.0
1	55	21.4	20.6	20.0	19.3	23.9	23.0	22.4	21.8
2	52	21.1	20.4	19.7	19.1	23.7	22.8	22.2	21.5
3	48	20.9	20.1	19.5	18.9	23.4	22.5	21.9	21.3
4	45	20.6	19.9	19.3	18.7	23.1	22.3	21.7	21.0
5	41	20.4	19.7	19.1	18.5	22.9	22.0	21.4	20.8
6	38	20.1	19.5	18.9	18.3	22.6	21.8	21.2	20.6
7	34	19.9	19.2	18.6	18.0	22.3	21.5	21.0	20.4
9	27	19.4	18.8	18.2	17.6	—	21.3	20.7	20.1
8	31	19.6	19.0	18.4	17.8	—	—	20.5	19.9
10	23	19.1	18.6	18.0	17.4	—	—	—	19.6

CHART 6

Chart 7: At 5,500 ft. and 2,450 RPM, you have 65% rated power, should obtain approximately 123 mph true airspeed, have an endurance of 6.8 hrs., and a range of 837 miles.

Use cruise performance charts to plan refueling stops. If you learn that your airplane performs differently than predicted by the chart, use this information; especially when performance is worse than predicted by the chart.

WHAT CAN YOU LEARN FROM STALL SPEED CHARTS? Chart 8 is a typical example of a Stall Speed Chart taken from an airplane flight manual. Note and continually be aware of the wide variation in stall speed between straight-and-level flight and various angles of bank. Note that the stall speed in a 60° bank with flaps up and power off (102 mph) is almost double the stall speed in straight-and-level flight with flaps down and power on (55 mph). Even with power on in the 60° bank, the stall speed is reduced only 4 mph to 98 mph. Study this chart and be aware of its significance, especially during traffic patterns and landings. You will find similar charts in any airplane flight manual.

STALL SPEEDS IAS

CONFIGURATION	0°	ANGLE OF BANK 20°	40°	60°
Flaps Up — Power Off	72 mph	74 mph	82 mph	102 mph
Flaps Up — Power On	69 mph	71 mph	79 mph	98 mph
Flaps Down (30°) — Power Off	64 mph	66 mph	73 mph	91 mph
Flaps Down (30°) — Power On	55 mph	57 mph	63 mph	78 mph

CHART 8

WHAT CAN YOU OBTAIN FROM LANDING PERFORMANCE CHARTS? The same type of information that you get from Takeoff Performance Charts--distance required to clear a 50-foot obstacle, length of the ground run, and in some cases, the recommended approach speed on which these figures are based. Landing Performance Charts will generally be used in the same way as Takeoff Charts for any given airplane, since each manufacturer usually follows the same format in these two charts. If you can read Takeoff Charts, you should have no difficulty reading Landing Charts.

HOW CAN YOU OBTAIN VALUES FROM PERFORMANCE CHARTS FOR CONDITIONS INTERMEDIATE TO THOSE GIVEN? By interpolation. For example, in Chart 1 (page 1) find the ground run required at an elevation of 5,000 ft., 72.5°F, zero wind, and maximum gross weight:

Ground run at 4,000 ft., 75°F, zero wind = 1,380 ft.   1,640 - 1,380 = 260
Ground run at 5,000 ft., 72.5°F, zero wind =   ?   1/2 x 260   = 130
Ground run at 6,000 ft., 70°F, zero wind = 1,640 ft.   1,380 + 130 = 1,510

Since 5,000 ft. is halfway between 4,000 and 6,000 and the temperature is halfway between 75° and 70°, the ground run should be halfway between 1,380 and 1,640, which is 1,510.

Find the distance to clear a 50-foot obstacle at 4,000 ft., 65°F, zero wind, and maximum gross weight:

Distance at 4,000 ft., 45°F, zero wind = 1,810 ft.   2,065 - 1,810 = 255
Distance at 4,000 ft., 65°F, zero wind =   ? ft.   2/3 x 255   = 170
Distance at 4,000 ft., 75°F, zero wind = 2,065 ft.   1,810 + 170 = 1,980

Since 65° is two-thirds of the way between 45° and 75°, the distance should be two-thirds of the way between 1,810 and 2,065 which is 1,980 ft.

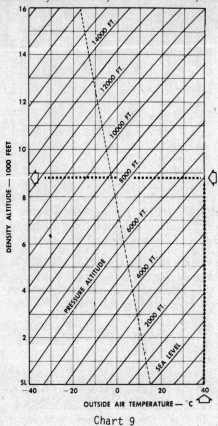

Chart 9

IF INTERPOLATION IS DIFFICULT OR YOU ARE IN DOUBT ABOUT YOUR COMPUTATION, HOW CAN YOU ENSURE BEING ON THE SAFE SIDE? Use a condition more adverse than the one that actually exists--one that you can read directly from the chart without interpolating. Suppose, for example, you were taking off from an airport at an elevation of 5,200 ft. with a 5 mph headwind, a temperature of 65° F, and maximum gross weight. By using an elevation of 6,000 ft., a zero mph wind, and 70° F, you can read the takeoff distance directly from Chart 1. The conditions you are using are more adverse than the actual conditions. If the results indicate that takeoff is feasible, then you should have no difficulty taking off under the actual conditions.

(NOTE: Charts 1, 3, 5, 6, and 7 are excerpts from charts. Charts 2, 4, 8, and 9 are complete. Charts 1, 2, and 4 have been reduced.)

Chart 9: Density Altitude Chart. At an elevation of 5,000 ft. (assuming pressure altitude and elevation are identical) and a temperature of 40° C (104° F) the density altitude is approximately 8,750 ft.

-4-

MIXTURE CONTROL--FUEL/AIR RATIO

It is generally conceded by most leading aircraft engine manufacturers that correct use of the mixture control in flight for adjusting the fuel/air ratio (F/A) is one of the most important items in the operation of aircraft engines. This Exam-O-Gram explains some of the related factors which should be considered when leaning the fuel/air mixture. It is hoped that this brief discussion will serve as a stimulus for pilots to study and search for more information on this subject--in aircraft power plant manuals-- and especially the engine manual pertinent to the aircraft they are operating. Certain General Aviation Written Examinations contain test items which are concerned with the results of improper use of mixture control.

The mixture control knob in an aircraft cockpit is usually RED--an indication that it should be used with "caution." Proper leaning of the mixture provides smoother engine operation, more power for a given power setting, best range and endurance; on the other hand, misuse of the mixture control can soon ruin an aircraft engine.

WHAT DOES FUEL/AIR (F/A) RATIO MEAN? It is the ratio between the weight of the fuel and the weight of the air that goes into the cylinders. In general, gasoline engines require approximately 15 pounds of air in order to completely burn 1 pound of gasoline. However, a theoretically perfect mixture ratio is not essential or desired in all cases. Certain conditions may require the use of mixture either richer or leaner than this average ratio. Usually, the useful mixture ratios are between 1 to 11 and 1 to 16. Fuel and air proportions are expressed on the basis of weight rather than volume. Fuel/air ratios may be given as a direct ratio, such as 1 to 12, but in more common usage, they are designated as decimal fractions such as 0.083. For example: $1 \div 12 = 0.083:1$ (0.083 lb. of fuel to 1 lb. of air).

WHAT IS THE FUNCTION OF THE CARBURETOR? It measures the correct quantity of fuel to be supplied to the engine, ATOMIZING and MIXING the fuel with air in the correct proportion (F/A ratio) before the mixture enters the cylinders. This proportioning must be done correctly regardless of the speed, load, and altitude at which the engine is operating. Gasoline cannot ignite or burn when in the liquid state, it first must be vaporized and mixed with the correct amount of air before it can be ignited and combustion takes place. When compared to other gasoline engines, aircraft engines operate at a greater altitude range and therefore are equipped with manual and/or automatic mixture controls.

HOW ARE CARBURETORS NORMALLY CALIBRATED? They are calibrated for sea-level operation, which means that the correct mixture of fuel and air will be obtained at sea level with the mixture control in the "full rich" position. As we climb to higher altitudes, the air density decreases--that is, a cubic foot of air will not weigh as much as it would at a lower altitude. Therefore, the weight of air entering the carburetor will decrease, although the volume remains the same. The amount of fuel entering the carburetor depends on the volume of air and not the weight of air. As the altitude increases, the amount of fuel entering the carburetor will remain approximately the same for any given throttle setting. Since the same amount (weight) of fuel is entering the carburetor, but a lesser amount (weight) of air, the fuel-air mixture becomes richer as altitude increases.

WHAT DOES THE MIXTURE CONTROL DO? It compensates for the decreased air density by metering the amount of fuel that passes through the main jet in the carburetor. In the less dense air at higher altitudes, a leaner mixture reduces fuel consumption and provides smoother engine operation. The mixture control is used to reduce the amount of fuel flow and maintain the proper F/A ratio-- this is also true of engines with fuel injection.

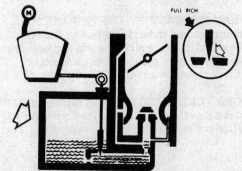

Needle Type Mixture Control System

AT WHAT F/A RATIO DO THE HIGHEST CYLINDER TEMPERATURES OCCUR? The greatest heat occurs at a fuel to air ratio of 1 to 15, or .067, and this is known as stoichiometric mixture (pronounced like stoy-key-o-metric), which is the chemically correct mixture where all the air and all the fuel is burned. Even though an F/A ratio of .067 is considered a chemically correct mixture for combustion, it produces peak temperatures and this is generally the mixture which will cause all gasoline engines to run the hottest (see Illustration below).

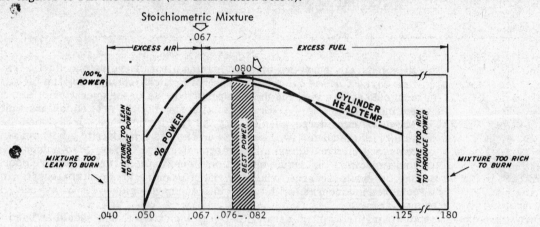

Fuel-Air Ratios vs Power & Temperature

The mixture of .067 is a theoretical point that can be demonstrated only on a single cylinder engine in a laboratory. In engines with more than one cylinder, the variations in fuel distribution between the cylinders makes it difficult to evaluate the F/A ratio in each cylinder. This matter of distributing equal amounts of fuel and air to the various cylinders is one of the greatest problems facing the aircraft engine manufacturers--or the designer of any gasoline engine for that matter. Because of the unequal Fuel/Air ratio in the various cylinders, the pilot who practices using extremely lean mixture settings without reference to proper instrumentation can experience a situation where all cylinders on his engine are operating at normal temperatures--except for one hot cylinder, where the exhaust valve and seat are red hot.

WHAT IS THE "BEST POWER" MIXTURE? The .080 fuel/air ratio is known as the "Best Power" mixture and it is that ratio at which the most power can be obtained for any given throttle setting. "Best Power" mixture is the fuel/air ratio where we can get a given power with the lowest manifold pressure or throttle setting. (See Illustration above.)

WHAT DOES EXCESS AIR AND EXCESS FUEL MEAN IN THE ILLUSTRATION? The illustration shows "Excess Air" on the left side of the .067 mixture, which means there is more air in the cylinders than is needed for normal combustion, and this excess of air absorbs heat and helps to cool the engine. On the right side of .067 mixture, we have "Excess Fuel" which means that there is more fuel in the cylinders than is needed for normal combustion, and this "Excess Fuel" also absorbs heat and provides additional cooling. Large supercharged engines can operate in the "Excess Air" lean mixture side of the .067 mixture, whereas the carburetor equipped, unsupercharged small aircraft engine should never be leaned to this extent. For example: If the manual mixture control of a supercharged engine is moved toward the lean position, cylinder head temperatures will be greatest when the F/A ratio is .067 and as the mixture is leaned still further, cylinder head temperatures will return to cooler normal values. When cylinder head temperatures climb too high while leaning carburetor equipped, unsupercharged engines, the mixture must be richened in order to return to cooler head temperatures.

WHAT IS MEANT BY UNEVEN MIXTURE DISTRIBUTION? In a carburetor equipped engine, the intake manifolds and induction pipes are used to distribute the fuel and air charge to the various cylinders. Those cylinders which are the farthest from the carburetor often receive a slightly leaner mixture than those cylinders close to the carburetor. When the mixture control is used to lean the mixture, the cylinders which are already receiving a leaner mixture will be the first ones to run hot or misfire.

DOES FUEL INJECTION PROVIDE BETTER FUEL DISTRIBUTION? Yes, the fuel is injected into the intake manifold and it is mixed with air just before entering the cylinders. Theoretically, all of the cylinders of a fuel injection engine are receiving an equal amount of fuel.

NOTE: Fuel injection engines are equipped with Fuel Flow Gauges to indicate the F/A mixture being supplied to the engine. Some of these instruments also show the percentage of power being used. Proper mixture control and better economy in the operation of a fuel injection engine can be achieved best through the use of an Exhaust Gas Temperature Indicator, a Cylinder Head Temperature Gauge and an Oil Temperature Gauge. The two latter instruments have slow response times but the trend of these basic heat references are very meaningful.

WHAT ARE THE RESULTS OF HAVING THE MIXTURE TOO LEAN? When the mixture is too lean there is too little fuel for the amount of air--in terms of weight. Rough engine operation, sudden "cutting out" or "back firing," detonation, overheating, or an appreciable loss of engine power may occur. Lean mixtures must be avoided when an engine is operating near its maximum output.

AT WHAT ALTITUDE IS LEANING THE MIXTURE NORMALLY EFFECTIVE? Leaning is normally effective above 5,000 feet; however, some aircraft engines may be leaned below 5,000 feet. Always follow the manufacturer's recommendations on leaning the fuel mixture for the particular airplane. By leaning the mixture at too low an altitude or leaning the mixture excessively, you could damage the engine at a high power setting. For example: Suppose that a pilot had been cruising at 8,000 feet with a lean mixture and forgot to move the mixture to full rich before entering the traffic pattern of a low elevation airport. The pilot may experience a rough engine or the engine might "cut out" or even worse if he were to exceed approximately 70% power in the pattern or on a go-around he would be in serious trouble with detonation and engine overheating. In general, lean mixtures must be employed with caution when operating aircraft engines at high power settings.

WHY IS 5,000 FEET CONSIDERED A SAFE ALTITUDE FOR LEANING? Certain aircraft engine manuals state that their engines should not be leaned below 5,000 feet. At 5,000 feet the unsupercharged engine is capable of developing only about 75% of its rated power, and at less than 75% power it is much harder to get into trouble using improper leaning techniques, since the cylinders and other engine parts are operating at lower temperatures.

WHAT IS DETONATION? Detonation is the spontaneous explosion of the unburned charge (in the cylinders) after normal ignition. If the temperature and pressure of the unburned portion of the fuel-air charge reach critical values, combustion will begin spontaneously. The result is a sudden and violent explosion of the charge (detonation) rather than the relatively slow burning of normal combustion.

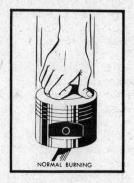
NORMAL BURNING

DETONATION

Continued operation when detonation is present can result in dished piston heads, collapsed valve heads, broken rings, or eroded portions of valves, pistons, or cylinder heads, and may terminate in sudden and complete engine failure.

Since it is very important to avoid detonation, it is well to consider the principal factors which contribute to this condition. The anti-knock value of the fuel (octane rating-performance no.), cylinder head temperature, incoming mixture temperature, fuel-air ratio, and intake manifold pressure are the most important factors of greatest significance for the pilot.

Usually detonation cannot be recognized from the cockpit through sound or engine roughness; therefore, protection from its possible occurrence must be provided by the design of the engine and adherence to the engine operating limitations.

WHAT IS PRE-IGNITION? Pre-ignition is the uncontrolled firing of the fuel-air charge in advance of normal spark ignition. It is caused by the presence within the combustion chamber of an area which is incandescent (red hot, glowing, luminous, with intense heat) and serves as an ignitor in advance of normal ignition. Pre-ignition may result from a glowing spark plug electrode, exhaust valve, or perhaps a carbon or lead particle heated to incandescence. As with detonation, such operating factors as high intake air temperatures, lean mixtures, high manifold pressures, and improper cooling are likely to set the stage for pre-ignition. Pre-ignition may start detonation, and paradoxically, detonation may start pre-ignition because of the high temperatures involved. Moreover, pre-ignition can be fully as destructive as detonation.

HOW IS ADDITIONAL FUEL PROVIDED FOR COOLING THE ENGINE ON TAKEOFF? At full power on takeoff with the mixture "full rich" you are assured of the best combination of power and cooling. The enrichment of the fuel-air mixture at high-power output is accomplished in actual carburetor design by the incorporation of auxiliary fuel-metering devices. Such devices are variously known as economizers, high speed jets, enrichment jets, power compensators, etc. Regardless of the name applied, all such units serve the same general purpose--that is, when full power is used on takeoff, the enrichment jets or valves cut in and provide additional fuel. This additional fuel helps to cool the engine during maximum power operation.

WHAT ARE THE RESULTS OF USING AN EXCESSIVELY RICH MIXTURE AT HIGH ALTITUDES?
Whenever an unsupercharged engine is operated at a high altitude with an excessively rich mixture, the power will be reduced from that which is available at that altitude with proper mixture. Excessive fuel is not required for combustion chamber cooling at high altitudes. The fouling of spark plugs is one of the greatest "bad effects" of operating with an excessively rich mixture. Spark plugs are designed to operate within certain heat ranges in order to function properly and operate without fouling. The excessively rich mixture will cause a below normal temperature of the spark plug center electrode, which, in turn, results in the formation of carbon and lead deposits. These deposits are electrically conductive and when they reach a sufficient depth, the electric current will flow through the deposit rather than "jumping-the-gap" in the spark plug to ignite the fuel air charge. This is what is known as a "fouled" or "shorted out" plug, since the current flows across the deposits on the ceramic insulator and is grounded instead of jumping the gap. Therefore, it is essential to maintain a fuel-air ratio which will provide sufficient heat in the combustion chamber to vaporize any deposits which may form on the ceramic center of the spark plug.

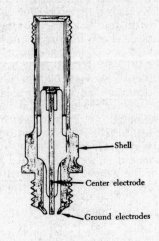

Shell

Center electrode

Ground electrodes

Radio Shielded Spark Plug

• • • • •

FOLLOW THE MANUFACTURER'S RECOMMENDATIONS
ON LEANING THE MIXTURE.

- 4 -

To test the applicant's knowledge of the practical aspects of cross-country flying, FAA written examinations contain test items on the use of radio aids to VFR navigation. In analyzing applicant performance on written examinations, it is apparent that a high percentage of applicants lack an adequate understanding of Automatic Direction Finding (ADF) procedures. Since a large number of modern aircraft are ADF equipped, it is essential that VFR pilots have a reasonable knowledge of the use that can be made of this important navigational aid. Since there is very little instructional material available to the VFR pilot in this area of knowledge, the material which follows is pertinent, timely, and promotes aviation safety.

The methods presented here are only the basic and more common uses of ADF suitable for VFR flights where "pin point" precision is not a vital factor. These methods include how to (1) fly to the station, (2) determine the direction of your position from the station, and (3) determine the ADF indication that signifies arrival at a desired direction from the station.

WHAT TYPE OF RADIO STATIONS CAN BE USED FOR ADF? Most ADF receivers receive signals in the frequency spectrum of 190 KHz (Kilo Hertz) to 1750 KHz, which includes LF (low frequency) and MF (medium frequency) navigation facilities, and the AM (amplitude modulation) commercial broadcast stations. Primarily for air navigation, the LF/MF stations are FAA and private non-directional radio beacons (Rbn), ILS compass locators (LOM), and four-course radio ranges (MRA). Marine radio beacons can be used but present difficulties in air navigation because they transmit only at brief scheduled periods and are arranged in groups of three or more along the coast, with each in the group transmitting on the same frequency. AM stations, or standard broadcast stations, are useful for air navigation; but remember that they can be identified only when the broadcast is interrupted for "station identification," some operate only during daylight hours, and many of the low-powered stations transmit on identical frequencies causing erratic ADF indications.

HOW DOES AN ADF INSTRUMENT INDICATE DIRECTION TO THE STATION? As implied by its nickname "Bird Dog," the ADF has automatic direction qualities which result in the indicator always pointing to the station to which it is tuned. This action is presented to the pilot on the vertically mounted face of the instrument (Fig. 1 and 2); that is, when the pointer is straight up (nose position), the station is ahead of the aircraft; when the pointer is straight down (tail position), the station is behind the aircraft; and when pointing 90° to either side (wing tip position), the station is off the respective wing tip.

WHAT DOES THE ADF INDICATION MEAN IN TERMS OF BEARINGS TO THE STATION? The more commonly used ADF instrument (sometimes termed Radio Compass), to which this Exam-O-Gram relates, has a stationary azimuth dial graduated up to 360° (with 360 or 0 at the top of the instrument representing the aircraft nose). The bearing pointer shows only the relative bearing, or angle from the nose of the aircraft to the station; i.e., the Relative Bearing in Fig. 1 is 060°. A more sophisticated instrument called a Radio Magnetic Indicator (RMI) uses a 360° azimuth dial which, being slaved to a gyro compass, turns with the aircraft to continually show the Magnetic Heading of the aircraft at the top of the instrument. With this rotating azimuth thus referenced to a magnetic direction, the bearing pointer superimposed on the azimuth, then indicates the Magnetic Bearing to the station. For example, in Fig. 2, the Magnetic Heading is 240°; the Magnetic Bearing to the station shown by the No. 1 needle, is 104°. The No. 2 needle shows a Magnetic Bearing of 040° to another station.

Fig. 1

Fig. 2

HOW CAN ADF BE USED TO FLY TO THE STATION? The easiest, and perhaps the most common method, is to "home" to the station. Since the ADF pointer always points to the station, simply head the aircraft so that the pointer is on the 0° or nose position. The station, then, will be directly ahead of the aircraft. With a crosswind, however, the aircraft would continually drift and, unless a change in heading is made, would no longer be headed straight to the station. This would be indicated by the pointer moving to the windward side of the nose position. By turning into the wind (toward the pointer) so as to continually return the pointer to the 0° position, the aircraft is flown to the station, although in a curving flight path, as shown in Fig. 3 inbound. (As this curving flight path deviates from the direct course, use caution to avoid drifting into unanticipated obstructions or terrain.) The lighter the crosswind and the shorter the distance, the less the flight path curves. Upon arrival at and passing the station, the pointer will swing from a nose position to a tail position.

IS IT POSSIBLE TO "HOME" AWAY FROM THE STATION? For all practical purposes--NO! "Homing" away from the station can be accomplished only if there is no crosswind. Attempting to keep the station directly behind the aircraft in a crosswind by turning to keep the pointer on the tail or 180° position, requires that the aircraft be turned more and more to a downwind heading. This, of course, results in the aircraft getting further and further from the desired course (Fig. 3 outbound).

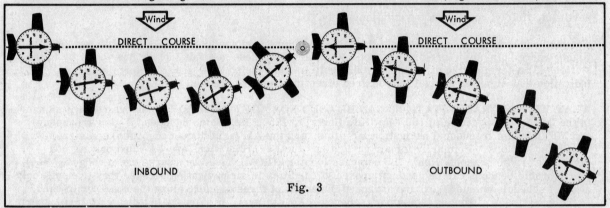

Fig. 3

OF WHAT IMPORTANCE IS THE MAGNETIC HEADING OF THE AIRCRAFT WHEN USING ADF? ADF should be considered as a moving, "fluid" thing. The number to which the indicator points on the fixed azimuth dial does not mean anything directionally until it is related to the aircraft's heading. Due to this relationship, the heading must be observed carefully when reading the Relative Bearing-to-the-station. Anytime the heading is changed, the Relative Bearing will be changed an equal number of degrees.

HOW CAN THE MAGNETIC BEARING TO A STATION BE DETERMINED ON A FIXED ADF AZIMUTH DIAL? Looking at the ADF instrument, imagine yourself as being in the center of the fixed azimuth, with the nose of the aircraft at the 0° position, the tail at the 180° position, and the left and right wing tips at the 270° and 090° positions respectively. When the pointer is on the nose position you are heading to the station and the Magnetic Bearing can be read directly from your compass (plus or minus deviation). If the pointer is left or right of the nose, note the direction and number of degrees of turn that would (if you were to head to the station) move the pointer to the nose position, and mentally apply this to your heading. For example, in Figure 4, a turn 60° to the left would place the pointer on the nose position. 60° left of the 090° Magnetic Heading is a Magnetic Bearing of 030° to the station. Your location, then, is southwest of the station, and if you were to head to the station, your heading would be 030°.

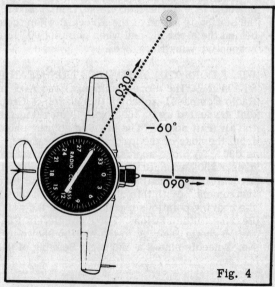

Fig. 4

- 2 -

**HOW CAN THE MAGNETIC BEARING FROM THE
STATION BE DETERMINED?** Since the direction from
the station is the opposite of the direction to the station,
it can be determined by following the steps discussed
in the preceding paragraph and add or subtract 180°, as
appropriate, to the aircraft-to-station bearing. In other
words, find the reciprocal of that bearing. If the ADF
pointer happens to be behind the wing-tip position (flying
away from the station), an alternate method is to note
the number of degrees and the direction of turn that
would move the pointer to the tail position, and apply
to the heading. For example, in Figure 5, a turn 45°
to the right would place the pointer on the tail position.
45° to the right of the 030° Magnetic Heading is a
Magnetic Bearing of 075° from the station (east-
northeast of the station). Just as "radials" always
extend outward from a VOR station in a magnetic
direction, the Magnetic Bearings from an ADF station should be thought of as "radials" of that ADF
station. It is important to determine the radial
(bearing from the station) because to locate your
position, the line of position must be plotted from
the known station location, as similarly done in VOR
orientation.

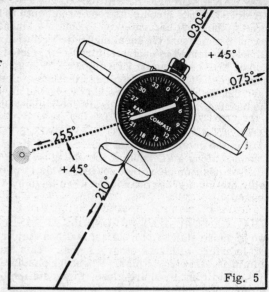

Fig. 5

**CAN THE ADF INDICATION WHICH SIGNIFIES ARRIVAL AT A SPECIFIC BEARING-TO-THE-
STATION BE PREDETERMINED?** YES! From the aeronautical chart, first ascertain whether the
station is left or right of the course being flown. Then, after selecting the Magnetic Bearing-to-the-
station that you desire to intercept, determine the angular difference between that bearing and your
Magnetic Heading (angle of intercept). With the aircraft headed to the 0° position of the ADF azimuth,
the bearing indicator, in pointing to the station, will show the relative angle between the aircraft's
nose and the station. As you continue on course this angle will gradually change, since the position of
the aircraft relative to the station is changing. Arrival at the preselected bearing-to-the-station will
be indicated when the pointer shows the difference between the heading and that bearing (angle of
intercept). For example, as shown in Figure 6, if your Magnetic Heading is to be 315° and the
selected bearing-to-the-station is 225°, the angular difference is 90° left. Arrival on this bearing
then, will be indicated when the pointer is 90° left of the nose position. If the station is to the right
of the course on a bearing of 045°, the 90° angle between the heading and the bearing would be shown
to the right of the nose position, as in Figure 7.

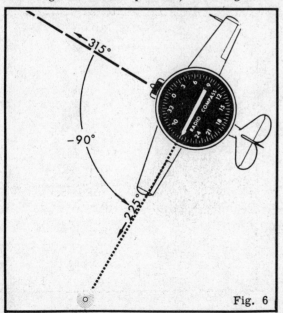

Fig. 6

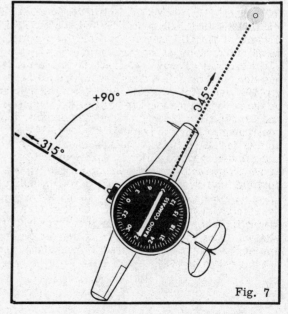

Fig. 7

HOW CAN MAGNETIC BEARINGS TO OR FROM A STATION BE DETERMINED ON AERONAUTICAL CHARTS? Since a compass rose or azimuth is not shown at LF/MF or AM stations on VFR-type charts, the most accurate way to obtain a Magnetic Bearing is to measure the direction with a plotter, taking into account the local magnetic variation. However, the many VOR azimuths and airway courses (already oriented to magnetic direction) printed on the chart can be used satisfactorily for approximation of ADF bearings on VFR flights. This approximation can be made on the basis of the direction of the nearest VOR radial or airway that most closely parallels the bearing of the ADF station. Remember, though, that the VOR radial or printed airway direction is <u>outbound from</u> the station. To find the bearing <u>to</u> the station, simply determine the reciprocal of the parallel radial or airway.

HOW CAN ADF BE USED TO SUPPLEMENT VOR NAVIGATION? One of the most valuable uses of ADF is the determination of your position along the course being flown. Even though you are following a course along a VOR radial, obtaining an ADF bearing that crosses the course will establish your "fix" or position along that course. This is particularly advantageous when an off-course VOR is not available for a cross bearing or when the only VOR receiver must be used as the primary tracking system.

WHAT CAN CAUSE AN ERRONEOUS ADF INDICATION? As mentioned earlier in this Exam-O-Gram, two or more standard broadcast stations may transmit on the same (or close to the same) frequency and interfere with each other's signal. This causes the ADF pointer to oscillate in an attempt to discriminate between stations. Whenever possible, choose stations of higher power and lower frequencies or wait until you are closer to the station before using it. Another source of erroneous bearings is improper tuning, or tuning in the fringes of a signal. Always tune to the center of the signal, which may be a few KHz (Kilo Hertz) on either side of the published frequency. And, of course, always make an <u>absolute identification</u> of the station before using it for navigation purposes. In the vicinity of electrical storms, the ADF pointer tends to swing from the radio station to the center of the storm at every flash of lightning. This makes it difficult to obtain reliable bearings. Erroneous or fluctuating bearings may also result from the deflection of radio waves from the surface of mountains. Use caution when taking bearings over mountainous terrain.

VISUAL APPROACH SLOPE INDICATOR (VASI)

Within the National Airspace System, there are many airports equipped with the standard Visual Approach Slope Indicators, and some are equipped with Abbreviated Visual Approach Slopes. The abbreviated systems contain fewer light units which may be installed on one side of the runway only. It is apparent that misconceptions and a lack of knowledge concerning this aid exist among the general aviation public. To assist those who are not familiar with VASI, particularly those taking FAA written tests, this Exam-O-Gram briefly explains the system, and answers questions commonly asked regarding the purpose, availability, and use of the device.

SYSTEM DESCRIPTION. The Visual Approach Slope Indicator (VASI) is a ground device which uses lights to define a predetermined visual glide path during the approach to a runway. As soon as the VASI lights are visible on final approach--day or night--a pilot receives the same information by visual reference that the glide slope unit of the Instrument Landing System (ILS) provides electronically. Once the principles and color code of the lighting system are understood, flying the VASI is as simple as looking out through the windshield and establishing and maintaining the proper rate of descent to stay on the glide slope.

This facility emits a visual light path within the final approach zone, at a fixed plane inclined from a minimum of $2\frac{1}{2}$° to a maximum of 4° from horizontal, which gives the pilot visual descent guidance during an approach to landing. The beam width is 15 degrees on each side of the extended runway centerline, but actual runway alignment is not provided by VASI. Course guidance to assure runway alignment should be obtained by reference to the runway lights, the runway itself, or by other approach aids.

Standard installation of the system requires twelve light-source boxes arranged in two split bars of light that straddle the runway. A set of 3 light units (boxes) is placed on each side of the runway approximately 600 feet from the threshold, and a second set of 3 is placed on each side at approximately the 1,300-foot point from the threshold. Formerly, these light unit arrays were known as the "downwind" and "upwind" light bars, respectively. Currently, however, the downwind bar is called the "near bar" and the upwind bar is known as the "far bar." The visual approach slope reference point is located midway between the far and near bars.

●●●

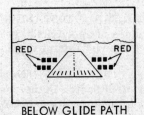

ABOVE GLIDE PATH   ON GLIDE PATH   BELOW GLIDE PATH

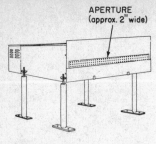

APERTURE
(approx. 2" wide)

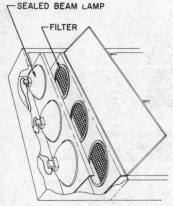

SEALED BEAM LAMP

FILTER

VASI LIGHT UNIT

LIGHT UNITS. Each light unit consists of a metal box 4.5 feet square and about 1 foot thick, housing three high intensity sealed beam lamps. Immediately in front of the lamps is a color filter assembly, the upper two-thirds of which is red and the lower portion is clear. Across the front of the box at the focal point of the lamps is a 2-inch aperture that extends across the width of the box. The "lens" effect, thus achieved, causes the light to appear white when viewed from a high angle, red when viewed from a low angle, and pink when viewed from the horizontal center of the aperture. The light intensity of each light unit is approximately 40,000 candlepower in the white light zone.

PRINCIPLE. The basic principle of VASI is that of color differential between red and white. The VASI provides obstruction clearance in the final approach area only. It is especially effective during approaches over water or featureless terrain where other sources of visual reference are lacking or misleading.

HOW ARE THE VASI APPROACH LIGHTS USED? For VFR conditions, proceed inbound maintaining normal traffic pattern altitude. When the near (downwind) bars transition from red through pink to white, commence descent. When on the proper approach path, the pilot is, in effect, overshooting the near bar light beam, and undershooting the far bar light beam. Thus, he sees the near bars as white and the far bars as red. When below the glidepath, both bars are red; when high, both bars are white.

Departure from the glidepath is indicated to the pilot by a transition in color of one of the light bars. If the departure is to the high side, the far bars will change from red through pink to white, leaving a completely white display. If the departure is to the low side, the near bar will change from white through pink to red, warning of a descent below the approach slope--by a completely red array of lights.

NOTE: Some deterioration of system guidance may occur as the pilot approaches the runway threshold due to the spread of light sources and narrowing of individual colors. However, the VASI will bring the pilot safely through a "gate" at the threshold where he may accomplish a normal flareout and landing. Since deterioration of system guidance occurs close in, the VASI is an <u>approach aid</u> rather than a landing aid.

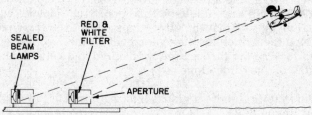

SEALED BEAM LAMPS

RED & WHITE FILTER

APERTURE

ABOVE GLIDE SLOPE (PILOT SEES WHITE/WHITE)

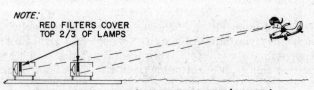

NOTE:
RED FILTERS COVER TOP 2/3 OF LAMPS

ON GLIDE SLOPE (PILOT SEES RED/WHITE)

WHAT ARE THE USABLE DISTANCES OF VASI? During daylight hours the VASI lights normally can be seen at distances of approximately 4 to 5 nautical miles. With bright sunlight or snow conditions the range is decreased. During the hours of darkness the lights may be seen at greater distances.

CAN THE LIGHT INTENSITY OF VASI BE ADJUSTED? Yes, the standard VASI system includes a light intensity control switch in the control tower. This remote control may be a two position "HIGH-LOW" switch or a three position "LOW-MEDIUM-HIGH" selector. If a pilot making a night VASI approach desired to have brightness of the lights turned down, he can request the controller in the tower to do so.

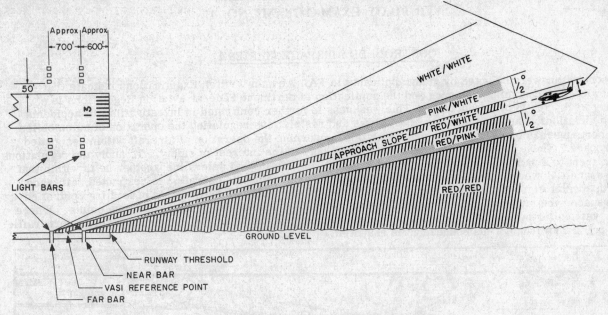

Glide path area approximately 97' in width at 4 nautical miles.

WHITE/WHITE
PINK/WHITE
RED/WHITE
APPROACH SLOPE RED/PINK
RED/RED
GROUND LEVEL

Approx 700' Approx 600'
50'
13
LIGHT BARS

RUNWAY THRESHOLD
NEAR BAR
VASI REFERENCE POINT
FAR BAR

TYPICAL VASI COLOR INDICATION PROFILE

WHAT ARE SOME OF THE FACTORS THAT AFFECT A PILOT'S COLOR INTERPRETATION? Such factors as snow, dust, precipitation, and color of background terrain affect the pilot's color interpretation of the VASI. Atmospheric conditions may distort the color the pilot is actually seeing or preclude the determination of a well-defined glide path or transition area. However, there is no distortion in the Red/Red area. When all lights are solid red, the aircraft is definitely below the glide slope.

HOW DOES A PILOT DETERMINE IF AN AIRPORT IS EQUIPPED WITH VASI? By referring to the Airport/Facility Directory listing for that airport. Note in the excerpt to the right that VASI equipment is provided for Runways 17 and 35. There is no VASI information listed on WAC or Sectional Charts, however, it does appear on the Instrument Approach Procedure Charts.

PONCA CITY MUNI (PNC) 1.7 NW GMT 6(-5DT) 36°43'41"N 97°06'00"W   WICHITA
1007 B S4 FUEL 100 JET A   CFR Index A   H-21, 3A, L-6H
RWY 17-35: H6201X150 (CONC-GRVD) S-51, D-65, DT-122 HIRL   IAP
RWY 17: REIL, VASI, rgt tfc. RWY 35: REIL, VASI
AIRPORT/FACILITY DIRECTORY Excerpt

WHEN ARE THE VASI LIGHTS IN OPERATION? The VASI shall normally be operated, day or night, when the runway it serves is the landing runway--or--when requested by the pilot.

ARE THERE ANY REGULATIONS THAT DEAL WITH VASI? Yes, FAR 91. 87 states in part: "(d) Minimum altitudes. When operating to an airport with an operating control tower, each pilot of --. . . . (3) an airplane approaching to land on a runway served by a visual approach slope indicator, shall maintain an altitude at or above the glide slope until a lower altitude is necessary for a safe landing." (NOTE: Regulations permit normal bracketing maneuvers above or below the glide slope that are conducted for the purpose of remaining on the glide slope.)

● ● ●

VASI provides unquestionable obstruction clearance in the approach area which is very comforting during night landings at strange airports. It reduces the chance of overshooting or undershooting, and it aids in making a landing in the first portion of the runway. VASI is also an effective noise abatement procedure where large airplanes and turbine-powered airplanes are concerned.

★ ★ ★ ★ ★

VFR PILOT EXAM-O-GRAM* NO. 41

CONTROLLED AIRSPACE (SERIES 1)

Incorrect answers selected by many applicants in FAA Airman Written Examinations indicate that knowledge of controlled airspace and the application of pertinent Federal Aviation Regulations is a very weak area in pilot education. This weakness is further confirmed in investigations of accidents and violations. Just as there are traffic laws and restrictions regulating the operation of automobiles in certain areas or zones, there are regulations governing the operation of aircraft within designated airspace. These regulated areas are established only in the interest of safety. To apply the regulations pertinent to a particular airspace, the pilot must first identify and determine whether he is within that airspace. However, unlike streets and highways where automobile operation is restricted, airspace with special flight restrictions has no posted signs or markers. Consequently, in locating controlled airspace, you must visualize it by correlating the chart symbols with ground reference points. Where the vertical or horizontal limits are not shown on the chart (for example, the limits of an airport traffic area), a knowledge of the boundaries is essential.

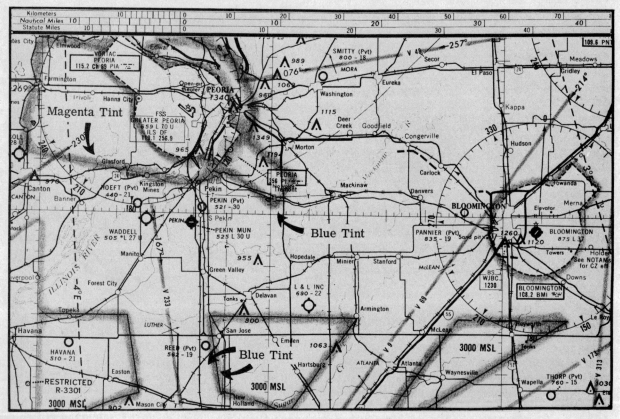

To assist in locating and identifying various controlled airspace, this Exam-O-Gram attempts to show in three-dimensional perspective, only that airspace closely related to VFR flights. While the dimensions of the airspace are indicated, the illustrations are not drawn in true proportions. An accurate and complete description of each airspace will be found in FAR Part 1, Definitions and Abbreviations, or Part 71, Designation of Federal Airways, Controlled Airspace and Reporting Points.

As you read this Exam-O-Gram relate each illustration to the Sectional Chart excerpt above; then consult the applicable regulation referenced in the accompanying text. Although each airspace has its individual boundaries and rules, you should remember that frequently one overlaps or is collocated with another, as in the case of an airport having an airport traffic area within a control zone. Appearing with each illustration are review questions dealing with VFR flights on the above chart segment. Check your answers against the answers and explanations given in the next Exam-O-Gram (No. 42).

AIRPORT TRAFFIC AREA - airspace within 5 statute miles of an airport at which a control tower is in operation. This airspace extends from the ground up to but not including 3,000 feet above ground level (AGL). The boundaries are not depicted on aeronautical charts but the presence of an airport traffic area is indicated when tower radio frequencies are shown in the airport data box. (Letters CT appear on new series Sectional Charts.) While this area is not designated as controlled airspace, the radio communications and operating requirements affect all flights taking off and landing at those airports.

Reference: FAR 1, 91.85, 91.87.

(Use chart excerpt on first page)

1. IS THERE AN AIRPORT TRAFFIC AREA AT GREATER PEORIA AND BLOOMINGTON AIRPORTS?

2. IF YOU HAVE NO RADIO, AND THE CEILING AND VISIBILITY ARE UNLIMITED (CAVU), ARE YOU PERMITTED TO LAND AT GREATER PEORIA? AT BLOOMINGTON?

3. WHEN OVERFLYING GREATER PEORIA AIRPORT AT 4,000 FEET MSL IN CAVU WEATHER, ARE YOU REQUIRED TO MAINTAIN TWO-WAY RADIO COMMUNICATIONS WITH THE CONTROL TOWER? AT 3,500 FEET MSL?

4. WHAT IS THE MAXIMUM AUTHORIZED SPEED FOR RECIPROCATING ENGINE AIRCRAFT WHEN APPROACHING GREATER PEORIA FOR LANDING?

CONTROL ZONE - airspace that is normally a circular area with a 5 mile radius and extensions as necessary for instrument approach and departure paths at certain airports. (A control tower may or may not be located within the control zone.) It starts at the surface, and extends up to the base of the Continental Control Area. The lateral limits are shown on aeronautical charts by a dashed line. Specific weather minimums are required for VFR flight within this zone, and an ATC clearance is required when the weather is less than VFR minimums. Certain other flight restrictions are also in effect within this airspace.

Reference: FAR 1, 71.11, 91.71, 91.105, 91.107.

(Use chart excerpt on first page)

1. WHAT WEATHER CONDITIONS MUST EXIST TO LAND OR TAKE OFF AT BLOOMINGTON WITHOUT OBTAINING A SPECIAL VFR CLEARANCE? AT GREATER PEORIA?

2. WITH WHOM WOULD YOU COMMUNICATE TO RECEIVE A SPECIAL VFR CLEARANCE AT GREATER PEORIA? AT BLOOMINGTON?

3. AT WHAT ALTITUDE ARE YOU PERMITTED TO PRACTICE STALLS, SPINS, OR ACROBATICS OVER BLOOMINGTON AIRPORT?

CONTROL AREA - designated airspace starting at 700 feet above ground level (unless a higher altitude is specified) and extending upward to the base of the overlying Continental Control Area (14,500 feet MSL). The lateral limits, normally identical to Federal Airways but frequently including far-reaching extensions, are shown on Sectional Charts with colored boundaries. Those areas bounded by magenta (purplish-red) tint start at 700 feet AGL, while those bounded by blue tint start at 1,200 feet AGL (unless a higher altitude is specified). The dark edges of tinted borders indicate the outer boundary of the airspace. VFR flights within control areas require certain weather minimums.

Reference: FAR 1, 71.7, 71.163, 91.105.

(Use chart excerpt on first page)

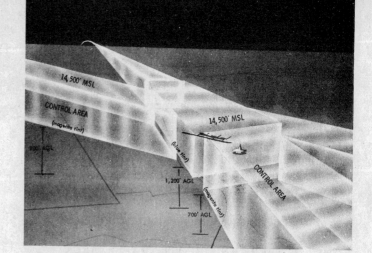

1. WHEN OVER THE TOWN OF MACKINAW (CENTER OF CHART) AT 3,000 FEET ABOVE THE GROUND, ARE YOU WITHIN CONTROLLED AIRSPACE?

2. WHEN FLYING IN THE IMMEDIATE VICINITY OF MACKINAW AT 15,500 FEET MSL WOULD YOU BE IN THE CONTROL AREA?

3. WHAT ARE THE VISIBILITY AND CLOUD CLEARANCE MINIMUMS WHEN FLYING VFR AT 9,500 FEET MSL IN THE IMMEDIATE VICINITY OF MACKINAW?

CONTINENTAL CONTROL AREA - Consists of the airspace of the 48 contiguous states, the District of Columbia, and Alaska south of latitude 68 degrees North, excluding the Alaska peninsula west of Longitude 160° West, at and above 14,500 MSL, but does not include (a) the airspace less than 1500 feet above the surface; and (b) certain prohibited or restricted areas.

Reference: FAR 1, 71.9, 91.105.

(Use chart segment on first page)

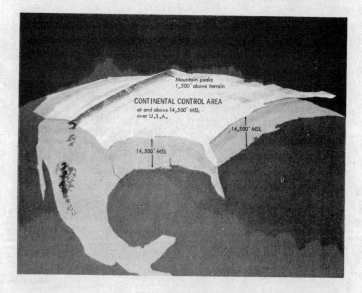

1. WHAT VISIBILITY IS REQUIRED TO FLY VFR AT 16,500 FEET MSL ON V 9 V 69 AIRWAY?

2. IF THERE ARE CLOUDS AT 17,000 FEET MSL, HOW FAR BELOW THE CLOUDS SHOULD YOU FLY ON V 9 V 69 AIRWAY VFR?

3. IF YOU ARE OUTSIDE THE LATERAL LIMITS OF AN AIRWAY AT 15,500 FEET MSL, WHAT ARE THE MINIMUM WEATHER CONDITIONS FOR VFR FLIGHT?

FEDERAL AIRWAY - each airway is based on a centerline that extends from one navigational aid or intersection to another navigational aid specified for that airway. The centerline is shown on aeronautical charts, and the magnetic course and the airway identity are indicated. Each airway includes airspace within parallel boundary lines normally 4 nautical miles each side of the centerline, and extends from 1,200 feet above the surface (unless a higher altitude is indicated) upward to, but not including 18,000 feet MSL. Airways in Hawaii have no upper limits. Inasmuch as a Federal Airway is controlled airspace divided at 10,000 feet MSL, VFR flight within the airway requires distinct weather minimums above and below 10,000 feet. Certain flight maneuvers are restricted in this airspace.

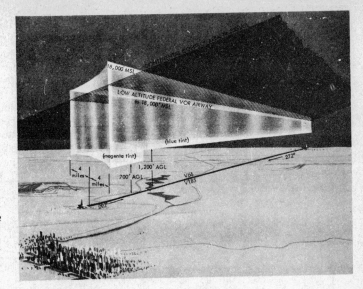

Reference: FAR 1, 71.5, 91.71, 91.105.

(Use chart excerpt on first page)

1. HOW FAR EAST OR WEST OF WADDELL AIRPORT (SOUTHWEST OF PEORIA) SHOULD YOU GO TO PRACTICE STALLS, SPINS, OR ACROBATICS?

2. IF YOU ARE FLYING VFR AT 15,500 FEET MSL ON V9 V69 AIRWAY (SOUTHWEST OF BLOOMINGTON), WHAT ARE THE MINIMUM VISIBILITY AND CLOUD CLEARANCE REQUIREMENTS? AT 3,000 FEET MSL?

3. WHAT MINIMUM VISIBILITY IS REQUIRED TO FLY VFR FROM WADDELL AIRPORT TO PEKIN MUNICIPAL AIRPORT AT 1,100 FEET MSL?

ANSWERS WITH EXPLANATIONS ARE PRESENTED IN EXAM-O-GRAM NO. 42.

CONTROLLED AIRSPACE (SERIES 2)

Illustrations and brief descriptions of airspace in which certain controls are imposed on VFR flights, along with references to pertinent Regulations, are presented in Exam-O-Gram No. 41. In addition, questions relating to a segment of a selected aeronautical chart are posed with the answers omitted, to inspire complete study of controlled airspace. Those questions are restated and the correct answers are briefly discussed in this Exam-O-Gram as an additional service to the reader.

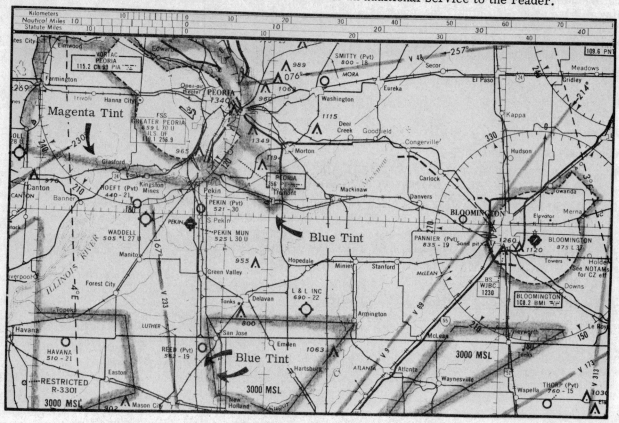

AIRPORT TRAFFIC AREA

1. **IS THERE AN AIRPORT TRAFFIC AREA AT GREATER PEORIA AND BLOOMINGTON AIRPORTS?**

   There is an Airport Traffic Area at Greater Peoria, but not at Bloomington. Remember that Airport Traffic Areas exist only at airports where control towers are in operation. In checking the airport data box for Greater Peoria, you will note radio frequencies, indicating the existence of a control tower and therefore an Airport Traffic Area when the control tower is in operation. The lack of frequencies at Bloomington Airport indicates there is no tower, so there is no Airport Traffic Area at that airport. Two-way radio communications are normally required for takeoff and landing at Greater Peoria, but not at Bloomington during VFR weather.

2. **IF YOU HAVE NO RADIO, AND THE CEILING AND VISIBILITY ARE UNLIMITED (CAVU), ARE YOU PERMITTED TO LAND AT GREATER PEORIA? AT BLOOMINGTON?**

   Yes. Because Greater Peoria has an Airport Traffic Area, radio communications are normally required for takeoff and landing. However, Regulations provide that if the radio becomes inoperative during flight, a landing may be made if the ceiling and visibility are at least 1,000 feet and 3 miles, after obtaining clearance to land by light signal (green light) from the tower.

Similarly, an aircraft not equipped with radio may land if prior approval (by telephone) is obtained from the control tower. Inasmuch as Bloomington has no control tower, (therefore no Airport Traffic Area) there are no requirements for radio communications or prior approval for landing when the weather meets basic VFR minimums.

3. WHEN OVERFLYING GREATER PEORIA AIRPORT AT 4,000 FEET MSL IN CLEAR WEATHER, ARE YOU REQUIRED TO MAINTAIN TWO-WAY RADIO COMMUNICATIONS WITH THE CONTROL TOWER? AT 3,500 FEET MSL?

At 4,000 feet MSL - no; at 3,500 feet MSL - yes. Airport Traffic Areas extend from the surface up to but not including 3,000 feet above the ground. Since the airport elevation is 659 feet, you would be above the Airport Traffic Area when at 4,000 feet MSL and would not be required to communicate with the tower. (If the flight visibility is less than 3 miles, however, communications would be required since this is also a Control Zone.) At 3,500 feet MSL, you would be in the Airport Traffic Area, since this altitude is within 3,000 feet of the ground, and you would be required to maintain two-way communications with the tower.

4. WHAT IS THE MAXIMUM AUTHORIZED SPEED FOR RECIPROCATING ENGINE AIRCRAFT WHEN APPROACHING GREATER PEORIA FOR LANDING?

Any time you are flying below 10,000 feet MSL, your indicated airspeed should be no more than 250 knots (288 MPH). When within the Airport Traffic Area, your airspeed should be no more than 156 knots (180 MPH).

CONTROL ZONE

1. WHAT WEATHER CONDITIONS MUST EXIST TO LAND OR TAKE OFF AT BLOOMINGTON WITHOUT OBTAINING A SPECIAL VFR CLEARANCE? AT GREATER PEORIA?

At least a 1,000-foot ceiling and 3 miles visibility at either of these airports. Note on the chart that both Bloomington and Greater Peoria airports lie within a Control Zone. A special VFR clearance is not required to operate within a Control Zone if the ceiling is at least 1,000 feet and the visibility is at least 3 miles. When the weather is below these minimums, but not less than one mile visibility, a special VFR clearance from ATC (Air Traffic Control) is required prior to operating in the Control Zone. (Visibility less than one mile requires an instrument clearance.)

2. WITH WHOM WOULD YOU COMMUNICATE TO RECEIVE A SPECIAL VFR CLEARANCE AT GREATER PEORIA? AT BLOOMINGTON?

With Peoria Tower at Greater Peoria, and Bloomington Radio at Bloomington Airport. To separate and coordinate IFR traffic and special VFR traffic, appropriate clearances are issued by the ATC (Air Traffic Control) facility serving each airport. At Greater Peoria these clearances are normally obtained through the control tower or approach control. Since a control tower is not located at Bloomington, clearances should be obtained by communicating with Bloomington Radio (controlled by Peoria FSS) who would obtain and relay the clearances from ATC.

3. AT WHAT ALTITUDE ARE YOU PERMITTED TO PRACTICE STALLS, SPINS, OR ACROBATICS OVER BLOOMINGTON AIRPORT?

Above 14,500 feet MSL only. Regulations prohibit the performance of those maneuvers within a Control Zone (as well as an airway). Bloomington Airport lies within a Control Zone and since this zone extends upward to the base of the Continental Control Area, those maneuvers would not be permitted at or below 14,500 feet MSL over Bloomington Airport.

CONTROL AREA

1. WHEN OVER THE TOWN OF MACKINAW (center of the chart) AT 3,000 FEET ABOVE THE GROUND, ARE YOU WITHIN CONTROLLED AIRSPACE?

Yes. At first it may appear on the chart that Mackinaw does no lie within controlled airspace. However, remember that the outer limit of controlled airspace is shown by the darker and more definite edges of the tinted boundaries and the vanishing, or feathered edges show the direction of the controlled airspace. Since the darker edges of the nearby controlled airspace boundaries face away from Mackinaw, and the vanishing edges face toward Mackinaw, it is apparent that this town lies in a Control Area. This particular Control Area starts at 1,200 feet above the ground (boundaries in blue tint); therefore at 3,000 feet above the ground you would be within the Control Area.

2. WHEN FLYING IN THE IMMEDIATE VICINITY OF MACKINAW AT 15,500 FEET MSL, WOULD YOU BE IN THE CONTROL AREA?

No. Control Areas extend from 700 feet or 1,200 feet (as designated) above the ground, upward to the base of the Continental Control Area. Since the Continental Control Area starts at 14,500 feet MSL, you would be in this overlying area (instead of the lower Control Area) when at 15,500 feet MSL.

3. WHAT ARE THE VISIBILITY AND CLOUD CLEARANCE MINIMUMS WHEN FLYING AT 9,500 FEET MSL IN THE IMMEDIATE VICINITY OF MACKINAW?

3 miles visibility and 1,000 feet above or 500 feet below and 2,000 feet horizontally from any cloud formation. We have established that the airspace surrounding Mackinaw between 1,200 feet above the ground and 14,500 feet MSL is a Control Area. Therefore, on a VFR flight at 9,500 feet MSL, you must have at least 3 miles visibility and remain at least 1,000 feet above or 500 feet below, and 2,000 feet horizontally from clouds. (Above 10,000 feet MSL anywhere, you must have at least 5 miles visibility and remain 1,000 feet above or below clouds.)

CONTINENTAL CONTROL AREA

1. WHAT VISIBILITY IS REQUIRED TO FLY VFR AT 16,500 FEET MSL ON V9 V69 AIRWAY?

At least 5 miles. The VFR visibility requirement is the same when at or above 10,000 feet MSL or in the Continental Control Area (above 14,500 feet MSL), regardless of whether you are on or off airways. Therefore, at 16,500 feet MSL on V9 V69, a VFR flight requires a visibility of 5 miles. **

2. IF THERE ARE CLOUDS AT 17,000 FEET MSL, HOW FAR BELOW THE CLOUDS SHOULD YOU FLY ON V9 V69 AIRWAY VFR?

At least 1,000 feet. When on an airway below 10,000 feet MSL, only 500 feet clearance beneath the clouds is required. However, at and above 10,000 feet or in the Continental Control Area (above 14,500 feet MSL) you are required to have at least 1,000 feet clearance beneath the clouds regardless of whether on or off airways. **

3. IF YOU ARE OUTSIDE THE LATERAL LIMITS OF AN AIRWAY AT 15,500 FEET MSL, WHAT ARE THE MINIMUM WEATHER CONDITIONS FOR VFR FLIGHT?

At least 5 miles flight visibility, since a flight at or above 14,500 feet MSL, on or off an airway, is within the Continental Control Area. Additionally, you cannot fly VFR at less than 1,000 feet above or 1,000 feet below and 1 mile horizontally from any cloud formation. **

FEDERAL AIRWAYS

1. HOW FAR EAST OR WEST OF WADDELL AIRPORT (SOUTHWEST OF PEORIA) SHOULD YOU GO TO PRACTICE STALLS, SPINS, OR ACROBATICS?

At least 5 miles east or 3 miles west. Waddell Airport lies within the 8-mile width of V233 airway and Regulations prohibit the performance of those maneuvers within a Federal Airway. To be outside the limits of the airway you must fly 5 miles east or 3 miles west of Waddell.

2. IF YOU ARE FLYING VFR AT 15,500 FEET MSL ON V9 V69 AIRWAY (SOUTHWEST OF BLOOMINGTON) WHAT ARE THE MINIMUM VISIBILITY AND CLOUD CLEARANCE REQUIRE-MENTS? AT 3,000 FEET MSL?

Flight at 15,500 feet MSL, on or off airways, is within the Continental Control Area, and above 10,000 feet MSL, where you must have at least 5 miles visibility and remain at least 1,000 feet above or 1,000 feet below and 1 mile horizontally from any cloud formation. When flying at 3,000 feet MSL on the airway you are in a Control Area and VFR flight requires that you have at least 3 miles visibility and remain at least 1,000 feet above or 500 feet below and 2,000 feet horizontally from any cloud formation.

-- -- -- -- -- -- -- -- -- -- -- -- -- -- -- --

** NOTE: Since the original printing of this Exam-O-Gram, the airspace at and above 18,000 feet MSL in the area involved in this particular chart segment, has been designated Positive Control Area. Flights under Visual Flight Rules are prohibited above 18,000 feet MSL in this area.

-- -- -- -- -- -- -- -- -- -- -- -- -- -- -- --

3. WHAT MINIMUM VISIBILITY IS REQUIRED TO FLY FROM WADDELL AIRPORT TO PEKIN MUNICIPAL AIRPORT AT 1,100 FEET MSL?

One mile visibility. Although a Federal airway lies between Waddell Airport and Pekin Municipal, and both airports are within the horizontal boundaries of a Control Area, the base of an airway or control area is never less than 700 feet above the surface. The elevation of the two airports and the terrain between them is approximately 500 feet, so at 1,100 feet MSL, you would be beneath the controlled airspace. Therefore, this flight can be made at 1,100 feet MSL under VFR with as little as 1 mile visibility.

○ ○ ○ ○ ○

VFR PILOT EXAM-O-GRAM° NO. 43

ATIS (AUTOMATIC TERMINAL INFORMATION SERVICE)

The Federal Aviation Administration is constantly striving to improve its service to the public. This Exam-O-Gram describes Automatic Terminal Information Service (ATIS) which has improved Air Traffic Controller effectiveness and relieved radio frequency congestion in many terminal areas. Because ATIS contributes to safety, FAA written tests may include questions on this subject.

WHAT IS ATIS? The continuous broadcast of recorded non-control information in selected high-activity terminal areas. It relieves frequency congestion by automating the repetitive transmission of routine but essential information on frequencies other than those normally used for airport traffic control. This service is presently being provided at many FAA tower-controlled airports.

WHAT KIND OF INFORMATION IS PROVIDED BY ATIS? Sky condition, visibility, wind, altimeter setting, instrument approach, and runway/s in use are continuously broadcast for the designated airport. NOTAMS, Airman Advisories, or other information pertinent to the airport will be included as appropriate.

HOW ARE ATIS BROADCASTS RECEIVED? By tuning to the appropriate frequency published on the sectional charts or in the Airport/Facility Directory as depicted above. This is a continuous broadcast on the voice feature of a TVOR/VOR/VORTAC located on or near the airport, or a discrete UHF/VHF frequency. ATIS broadcasts on VOR/VORTAC facilities may be interrupted by the FSS to reply to frequency limited aircraft if necessary. Where VFR arrival aircraft are expected to make initial contact with approach control, this fact and the appropriate frequencies may be broadcast on ATIS.

WHEN SHOULD THE ATIS BROADCASTS BE UTILIZED? Prior to requesting taxi clearance by departing aircraft and prior to reporting to the tower by arriving aircraft.

IS ATIS DESIGNED PRIMARILY FOR THE IFR PILOT? No! The information broadcast is applicable to all departing and arriving aircraft, VFR as well as IFR.

DOES THE ATIS BROADCAST CONSTITUTE A CLEARANCE TO TAXI FOR TAKEOFF OR A CLEARANCE TO LAND? No! Since only routine information is contained in these broadcasts, ATC clearances to taxi, take off, or land must be issued separately to the individual aircraft by the appropriate controller on the appropriate frequency.

WHAT ARE THE ADVANTAGES OF ATIS OVER THE LONG-STANDING METHOD OF INDIVIDUAL INSTRUCTIONS? There are three distinct advantages: First, extensive utilization of ATIS by pilots will greatly reduce the congestion on tower and ground control frequencies, and the routine workload on the controllers. This will allow the controllers to devote more time to the specific control of arriving and departing aircraft; second, the ATIS broadcast contains more information than the normal tower or ground control instructions for taxi, takeoff, or landing (i. e., weather, NOTAMS, etc.); and third, the pilot can receive this information when cockpit duties are least pressing and listen to as many repeats as desired. (This should be a great boon to student pilots or pilots who operate infrequently at tower controlled airports.)

WHAT DOES A TYPICAL ATIS BROADCAST SOUND LIKE? Sample broadcast --". . THIS IS TULSA INTERNATIONAL AIRPORT INFORMATION ECHO. FOUR THOUSAND SCATTERED, VISIBILITY SIX, HAZE, WIND ONE FIVE ZERO DEGREES AT ONE THREE. TEMPERATURE EIGHT ONE, DEWPOINT SIX FOUR. ALTIMETER TWO NINER EIGHT NINER. I L S RUNWAY ONE SEVEN LEFT IN USE. LANDING AND DEPARTURE RUNWAYS ONE SEVEN LEFT AND ONE SEVEN RIGHT. NOTAM, RUNWAY ONE TWO, THREE ZERO CLOSED TO ALL OPERATIONS. INFORM TULSA APPROACH CONTROL, TOWER, OR GROUND CONTROL ON INITIAL CONTACT THAT YOU HAVE RECEIVED INFORMATION ECHO. . "

WHAT ARE THE SPECIFIC PROCEDURES FOR UTILIZING ATIS BROADCASTS? The broadcast should be monitored prior to requesting taxi clearance or prior to requesting landing clearance. Arriving aircraft should monitor the broadcast well in advance of entering the Airport Traffic Area. Each ATIS broadcast will carry an identifying phonetic alphabet code word (Alpha, Bravo, Charlie, etc.). This code word is important. After receiving the ATIS broadcast, the pilot, on initial contact with ground control, tower, or approach control, should state he has the information and repeat the specific code word. Example -- ". . TULSA GROUND CONTROL, THIS IS BEECHCRAFT SEVEN FOUR SIX FOUR CHARLIE. ON TERMINAL RAMP, READY TO TAXI. I HAVE INFORMATION ECHO. OVER. . "

HOW OFTEN ARE ATIS BROADCASTS CHANGED? They are normally updated hourly. However, they will be updated more frequently should a significant change occur in the information. Each time the message is updated, the next phonetic alphabet code word will be used.

WHAT HAPPENS WHEN PILOTS REQUEST CLEARANCE WITHOUT ACKNOWLEDGING RECEIPT OF THE ATIS BROADCAST OR ACKNOWLEDGE BY A CODE WORD WHICH IS NOT CURRENT? In either case the controller will issue the normal taxi or landing information.

NOTE: Some pilots use the phrase "Have Numbers" in communications with the control tower. Use of this phrase means that the pilot has received wind and runway information ONLY and the tower does not have to repeat this information. It does not indicate receipt of the ATIS broadcast and should never be used for this purpose.

ATIS IS A VALUABLE SERVICE. ALL PILOTS ARE ENCOURAGED TO USE IT EXTENSIVELY.

VFR PILOT EXAM-O-GRAM° NO. 44

HOW HIGH THE CLOUDS?

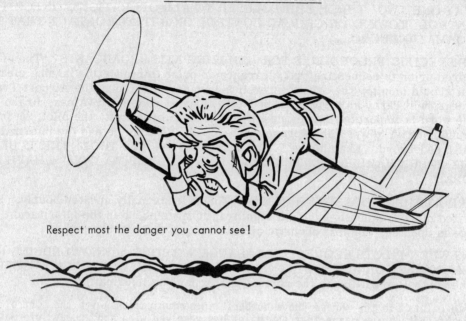

Respect most the danger you cannot see!

Analysis of results on FAA written tests reveal that frequently applicants do not properly interpret the height of clouds or ceilings as given in Aviation Weather Forecasts and Reports. Even more often, they are unable to relate these reports and forecasts of cloud and ceiling heights to altimeter indications and safe terrain clearance.

It may well ruin the balance of the day to learn that a written test was failed because of inability to determine the ceiling or to answer questions related to this knowledge, but there are even more serious consequences. General aviation accident statistics reveal that far more serious problems may be experienced if this same lack of knowledge prevails during flight operations.

Though not likely to improve the weather, perhaps the following questions and answers will help to clear up some of the aforementioned confusion.

TO WHAT IS THE HEIGHT OF THE BASES OF CLOUDS REFERENCED IN AVIATION WEATHER REPORTS, FORECASTS, AND BROADCASTS?

1. With certain exceptions which will be discussed later, cloud bases, whether they constitute a ceiling or not, are normally reported in feet above ground level.

2. Whenever a cloud base height is specifically designated "ceiling," it will always be with reference to above ground level. Ceiling heights are mentioned in Surface Aviation Weather Reports, Area Forecasts, Terminal Forecasts, In-flight Advisories, Transcribed Weather Broadcasts,   Weather Broadcasts. Also the cloud heights indicated on Surface Weather Charts and Weather Depiction Charts are above ground level.

NOTE: The contractions CLR, SCT, BKN, and OVC have replaced the symbols ○, ⊙, ⦶, and ⊕.

Examples (Excerpted)	Decoding:

Terminal Forecasts
C25 BKN 16Z BKN V OVC

Forecast ceiling 2500 feet broken variable to overcast <u>above the</u> surface (AGL).

Area Forecasts
20 SCT VRBL BKN TOPS 90

Base of clouds, variable scattered to broken, is forecast to be 2,000 feet <u>above sea level</u>. Tops of clouds forecast to be 9,000 feet <u>above mean sea level</u> (MSL). (Explained further in item 3 of next question.)

Hourly Weather Reports
15 SCT M30 OVC

Scattered clouds at 1,500 feet (above the surface), overcast ceiling measured at 3,000 feet (above the surface).

In-Flight Weather Advisories
AIRMET BRAVO 1. ON A LINE
FRM CRW THRU BKW TO ROA CONDS
LWRNG IN LGT RAIN & FOG TO
BLO 1 THSD FT AND BLO 2 MI
BFR 17Z WITH HIR TERRN OBSCD.
CONDS CONTG BYD 18Z.

On a line from Charleston through Beckley to Roanoke conditions lowering in light rain and fog to below 1,000 feet and below 2 miles before <u>1700Z</u> with higher terrain obscured. Conditions continuing beyond <u>1800Z</u>. (Ceilings are expected to be less than 1,000 feet above the surface.)

WHEN ARE CLOUD HEIGHTS NOT REPORTED IN FEET ABOVE THE SURFACE?

1. UA /OV CRW 13520 1620 FL055 /TP C210
/SK 35 BKN-OVC 95 /RM LGT TO MDT RAIN SHWRS

20 miles southeast of Charleston at 1620 GMT, at 5,500 feet, a C-210 pilot reported base of broken to overcast clouds at 3,500 feet, tops at 9,500 feet, light to moderate rain showers.

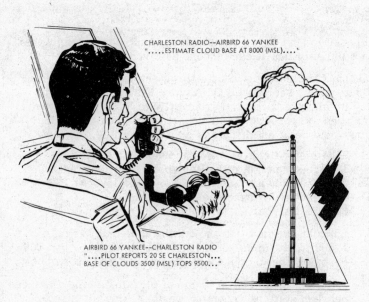

CHARLESTON RADIO--AIRBIRD 66 YANKEE
".....ESTIMATE CLOUD BASE AT 8000 (MSL)...."

AIRBIRD 66 YANKEE--CHARLESTON RADIO
"....PILOT REPORTS 20 SE CHARLESTON...
BASE OF CLOUDS 3500 (MSL) TOPS 9500..."

2. As in the preceding example, Pilot Weather Reports (PIREPS) give cloud heights in feet <u>above sea level</u>. Since flight altitudes are normally determined by reading an altimeter set to sea level pressure (MSL), all references to cloud heights are in feet above sea level. It is also true of turbulence, icing, and freezing levels. Note that the specific term "ceiling" is not used in the preceding PIREP.

3. As is the case with PIREPS, all cloud heights in Area Forecasts are normally given in feet <u>above sea level</u>. Such information is usually more useful to the enroute pilot when it is referenced to the same thing as his flight altitude or altimeter indication.

4. Occasionally, however, the height of cloud bases in Area Forecasts will be given in feet above the ground level. Ordinarily "above ground" references will be limited to descriptions of layers sufficiently near the ground to be of appreciable concern to VFR operations and to clouds formed primarily by convection turbulence. In such cases, the exception to the general rule stated in (3) is always noted in the forecast (HGTS ASL unless noted)

5. Although Terminal Forecasts and as previously noted, some Area Forecasts, give cloud <u>bases</u> in feet above the surface, references to cloud <u>tops</u> in Area Forecasts are based in heights above sea level. Terminal forecasts do not include information about cloud tops.

NOTE: A word of caution—remember that radar detects only thunderstorms and general areas of precipitation; it is <u>not</u> designed to detect enroute ceiling and visibility. An area may be blanketed with fog or low stratus, but unless precipitation is also present, the radar scope will be clear of echoes.

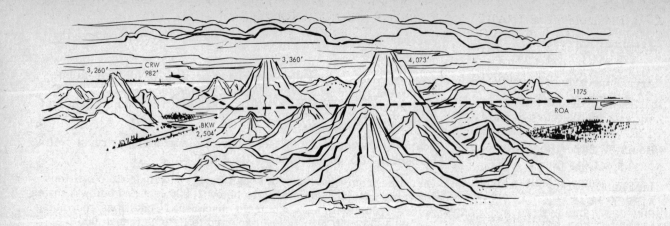

IF CLOUDS AND CEILINGS REMAIN AS GIVEN IN THE FOLLOWING AVIATION WEATHER REPORT EXCERPTS IS VFR FLIGHT FROM CHARLESTON TO ROANOKE VIA BECKLEY POSSIBLE?

Charleston, W. Va. (CRW) 45 SCT M50 OVC 5   LRG BINOVC
Beckley, W. Va. (BKW)   M12V BKN 3   HIR RDGS OBSCD   CIG 10V13 BKN V OVC
Roanoke, Va. (ROA)   M18 OVC 3   SUN DIMLY VSBL

1. NOT LIKELY! One cannot say that it is impossible, but in the mountainous country crossed by this flight, it is improbable, indeed. It is even more unlikely that it can be done safely.

2. A check of the illustration above will reveal that Charleston is 982 ft. above sea level, Beckley is 2,504 ft. above sea level, and Roanoke is 1,175 ft. above sea level. On Airway V-258 from CRW to BKW one mountain ridge is approximately 3,260 ft. above sea level. From BKW to ROA, other ridges are 3,360 and 4,073 ft. above sea level. If you were to approach to, or depart from Beckley, flying 500 feet below the clouds as reported above, you would be at an altitude of approximately 3,200 feet.

DIDN'T HE SAY THE CEILING WAS 2500 FEET?

2504 feet = field elevation at Beckley (MSL)
+1200 feet = height of ceiling above the ground at BKW
3704 feet = height of clouds above sea level at BKW
- 500 feet = clearance below the clouds
3204 feet = your flight altitude above sea level.

Ignoring the fact that the ceiling at Beckley is only 1,000 ft. at times, 3,204 ft. MSL is 56, 156, and 869 ft. below the tops of the 3 ridges mentioned previously.

3. When evaluated in terms of terrain and the distances between stations reporting weather, this situation obviously precludes any reasonable assumption that all enroute weather is likely to be VFR -- even though all stations report VFR weather. Note carefully that the remarks portion of the Beckley report states that the "higher ridges of the mountains are obscured."

4. Without specific pilot reports on enroute ceilings or other weather conditions, it would be reasonable to assume that clouds might be "on the deck" for portions of this flight.

IS THE PROBLEM DISCUSSED IN THE PREVIOUS QUESTION PECULIAR TO MOUNTAINOUS REGIONS?

No! ! The same problem exists in some measure, at least, in flat, open country - particularly during periods of rapidly changing weather and where there is considerable distance between weather reporting points. It is neither reasonable nor wise to assume that cloud bases along a flight route are uniform in height. Under the circumstances outlined, hourly Aviation Weather Reports alone do not afford enough information upon which to base a prudent decision that the flight can be safely accomplished.

A PIREP INDICATES THAT 27 MILES NW OF ROANOKE VORTAC ON V-258, THE BASE OF THE CLOUDS ARE AT 5,500. DOES THIS REFER TO HEIGHT ABOVE SEA LEVEL OR ABOVE THE GROUND? Refer to the PIREP discussion on page 2 for the answer.

WHAT IS THE APPROXIMATE CEILING AT THE POINT INDICATED IN THE PIREP?

1. Ceiling, by definition, refers to cloud height above the surface. It is impossible to determine height above the surface unless the surface elevation is also known. At the point stipulated in the PIREP, a check of a sectional chart will reveal that the terrain varies between 3,000 feet and 4,073 feet above sea level. Therefore, the ceiling could be anywhere between 2,500 and 1,427 feet.

2.   5500 feet = height of cloud base, MSL   5500 feet = height of cloud base, MSL
     -3000 feet = surface elevation, MSL   -4073 feet = surface elevation, MSL
      2500 feet = height of cloud base, AGL   1427 feet = height of cloud base, AGL

3. Admittedly, the illustration below is not too typical, but it effectively depicts the problem. Note that in one instance the ceiling is 6,000 feet; in another, it is only 1,000 feet. In fact, toward the left in the illustration the ceiling becomes zero, yet there has been no change in cloud height above sea level! Beware of this trap!

VFR PILOT EXAM-O-GRAM   NO. 45

AIRSPEEDS AND AIRSPEED INDICATOR MARKINGS (Series 2)

Most FAA written tests contain several test items involving airspeed. Analyses show that many applicants are not knowledgeable concerning airspeeds. The use of performance charts, computation of navigation problems, and filing of flight plans involves the use of True Airspeed. However, in various configurations and flight conditions, airplanes are also operated with reference to Calibrated Airspeed.

WHAT ARE THE DIFFERENT AIRSPEEDS?   The four principal airspeeds are defined below.

Indicated Airspeed (IAS) is the uncorrected speed read from the airspeed dial. It is the measurement of the difference between impact pressure and atmospheric pressure in the pitot-static system.

Calibrated Airspeed (CAS) is indicated airspeed corrected for instrument error and installation error in the pitot-static system. As the aircraft flight attitude or configuration is changed, the airflow in the vicinity of the static inlets may introduce impact pressure into the static source, which results in erroneous airspeed indications. The pitot section is subject to error at high angles of attack, since the impact pressure entering the system is reduced, when the pitot tube is not parallel to the relative wind. Note in the chart to the right the difference between indicated and calibrated airspeed in the lower speed ranges. Performance data in aircraft flight manuals is normally based on calibrated airspeed.

AIRSPEED CORRECTION TABLE

FLAPS	IAS	40	50	60	70	80	90	100	110	120	130	140
FLAPS UP	CAS	55	60	66	72	80	89	98	108	117	127	136
FLAPS DOWN	CAS	52	58	65	73	82	91	101	•	•	•	•

Equivalent Airspeed (EAS) is calibrated airspeed corrected for compressibility factor. This value is very significant to pilots of high speed aircraft, but relatively unimportant to pilots operating at speeds below 250 knots at altitudes below 10,000 feet.

True Airspeed (TAS) is calibrated airspeed (or equivalent airspeed if applicable) corrected for air density error. TAS is the actual speed of the aircraft through the air mass. Air density error is caused by nonstandard pressure and temperature for which the instrument does not automatically compensate. The standard airspeed indicator is calibrated to read correctly only at standard sea level conditions--that is, when the pressure is 29.92 inches Hg and the temperature is 15°C.

○ ○ ○ ○ ○

HOW IS TRUE AIRSPEED DETERMINED?   To find TAS, it is necessary to--(a) work a computer solution, or - (b) have in the aircraft an airspeed indicator, similar to the one illustrated to the left, which incorporates that portion of a computer which is necessary for determining TAS in the cruising speed range. This represents the current trend in the design of flight instruments that reduce pilot workload. In either case, the prerequisites for determining TAS are pressure altitude*, CAS, and outside air temperature. Example: For a pressure altitude of 6,500 feet, a CAS** of 175 mph, and an outside air temperature (OAT) of +20°C., you would use the instrument to the left as follows: With the adjusting knob, set the pressure altitude (6,500 feet) opposite the OAT (+20°C.). The needle then shows a TAS of 202 mph while on the inner portion of the dial the needle is registering an IAS of 175 mph or 152 knots.

OAT +20° C

*The most accurate method of solving for TAS is by use of pressure altitude. However, you can use indicated altitude without introducing too great an error in most instances.

**For this example the IAS and CAS are assumed equal.

Free air temperature gage

DO SOME INSTRUMENTS AUTOMATICALLY REGISTER TRUE AIRSPEED? Yes, more advanced true airspeed indicators contain components which correct for pressure altitude, OAT, and compressability to automatically provide TAS without computations on the part of the pilot.

WHAT ADDITIONAL AIRSPEED INDICATOR MARKINGS ARE REQUIRED IN MULTI-ENGINE AIRPLANES? FAR Part 23, which deals with Airworthiness Standards for airplanes of 12,500 lbs. or less, was amended November 11, 1965, to require the following airspeed markings in multi-engine airplanes: (a) a blue radial line to show the best rate of climb speed (V_y) with one-engine-inoperative. (b) a red radial line to show V_{mc} -the minimum control speed with one-engine-inoperative. Note in the illustration to the left, that these markings for key speeds in multi-engine airplanes are in addition to those normally required for other airplanes.

WHICH MULTI-ENGINE AIRPLANES ARE REQUIRED TO HAVE THESE MARKINGS? Only those airplanes which were type certificated under Part 23 on or after November 11, 1965, are required to have these markings. However, airplanes type certificated before that date may also be so marked at the option of the owner.

NOTE: The airspeed indicator markings may be either calibrated airspeed or indicated airspeed, depending on the manufacturer and age of the airplane. Presently, several aircraft manufacturers are substituting indicated airspeed for calibrated airspeed markings. Refer to the Pilot's Operating Handbook for your aircraft. Some handbooks state: "IAS values published in the handbook assume zero instrument error."

- 2 -

Color code for markings on the illustrations of airspeed indicators

  RED

BLUE

YELLOW

GREEN

VFR PILOT EXAM-O-GRAM° NO. 46

AVIATION WEATHER REPORT-REMARKS

FAA written tests require that applicants be knowledgeable in the weather information contained in teletyped Surface Aviation Weather Reports, necessary for planning and safely conducting cross-country flights. A study of test papers shows that weather related items are often answered incorrectly because certain available information is neglected.

A common misconception is that the regularly reported data alone, in the main body of the reports, reflects the overall weather situation at the reporting station. Frequently, remarks are added at the end of the report to cover unusual aspects of the weather, and often contain information which is as important as that found in the main body. The Remarks section is generally ignored by pilots who believe that the abbreviated information is difficult to interpret and meaningful only to meteorologists or air traffic control personnel. Admittedly, the coded NOTAMS (for example, → TUL↘3/47 XX 4/8 UR) also found in this section, are of particular significance to weather and traffic personnel and require special knowledge to decode. The weather remarks of importance to pilots, utilize standard abbreviations or contractions of words (BKN, OVC, RW, T, K, H, etc.). The few special code words used occasionally can be easily memorized. The contractions are formed by omitting vowels and other letters in a way that the meaning of the information remains obvious. For example, WND DRCTN VRBL T OVHD MOVG E should be read as WIND DIRECTION VARIABLE THUNDERSTORM OVERHEAD MOVING EAST.

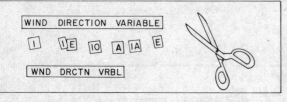

The abbreviations and contractions introduced in this Exam-O-Gram include only those which are most frequently used and most significant to pilots. Your ability to interpret abbreviated remarks will improve with practice. A partial list of standard remarks is provided on the reverse side of this page. Samples of typical reports, followed by translations of the Remarks section, are presented below for familiarization purposes. Note how, in these samples, the weather situation reported in the main body, takes on a different perspective when the remarks are considered in the overall weather picture. In the first report, the surface visibility of 20 miles looks good, but in reading further, we find the visibility at flight altitudes is reported to be restricted by smoke and haze.

SAMPLES OF COMPLETE REPORTS

1. DEN SA 1251 3ØØ SCT 2Ø 174/57/36/11Ø3/Ø15 TCU SW KH ALF.
2. ALS SA 1253 E5Ø BKN 12Ø BKN 4Ø 155/54/3Ø/2117/Ø15 HVY CB BD ALQDS.
3. ABQ SA 1254 E7Ø BKN 12Ø OVC 4Ø 111/68/55/1311/Ø1Ø MTN TOPS OBSCD W RWU N.
4. LIT SA 1253 45 SCT E1ØØ OVC 1Ø 133/7Ø/33/24Ø9/977 RB32E45 T E PRESFR.
5. ACT SA 1252 3Ø SCT E1ØØ BKN 15 Ø78/85/64/1815/985 LN CB SW-N OCNL LTGCG NW CB MAM N.

TRANSLATION OF REMARKS

1. towering cumulus clouds (TCU) southwest (SW), smoke (K), and haze (H) aloft (ALF).
2. heavy (HVY) cumulonimbus clouds (CB) and blowing dust (BD) in all quadrants (ALQDS).
3. mountain tops (MTN TOPS) obscured (OBSCD) west (W), rain showers (RW) of unknown intensity (U) north (N).
4. rain began (RB) 32 mins. after preceding hour, ended (E) 45 mins. after preceding hour, thunderstorm (T) east (E), pressure falling rapidly (PRESFR).
5. line (LN) cumulonimbus clouds (CB) southwest through north (SW-N), occasional (OCNL) lightning (LTG) cloud-to-ground (CG) northwest (NW), cumulonimbus mamma clouds (CB MAM) north (N).

The abbreviated remarks listed here serve only as an introduction to the manner in which weather conditions are often described in weather reports and forecasts. An expanded list of standard abbreviations and contractions is found in the publications, "Aviation Weather Services," AC 00-45A, and "Contractions Handbook" 7340.1. These can be purchased from the Superintendent of Documents, U.S. Government Printing Office, Washington, D.C. 20402. A manual containing currently-used contractions is also available for reference purposes at all weather briefing offices.

ACSL W-altocumulus standing lenticular clouds west.
BINOVC-breaks in the overcast.
CIG RGD - ceiling is ragged.
CU E-cumulus clouds east. (CB-cumulonimbus) (CB MAM-cumulonimbus mamma).
CFP-cold front passage. (FROPA-frontal passage).
D5-dust obscuring 5/10 of the sky.
FQT THDR NW - frequent thunder northwest.
KH ALF-smoke and haze aloft.
HIR CLDS VSB-higher clouds visible.
ICGIC-icing in clouds.
LN TSTMS E-line of thunderstorms east.
LTGIC-lightning in clouds. (CG-cloud-to-ground) (CC-cloud-to-cloud).
MTN RDGS OBSCD-mountain ridges obscured.
PRESFR-pressure falling rapidly. (RR-rising rapidly).
RADAT 75125 -(Radiosonde data) relative humidity 75% at lowest freezing level 12,500 feet.
RWU E-rain showers of unknown intensity east.
RB32-rain began 32 mins. after preceding hour. (E-ended).
TCU ALQDS-towering cumulus in all quadrants.
SQLN NW-squall line northwest.
VIRGA-precipitation falling but not reaching the ground.
OVC 65 -top of overcast is 6,500 feet MSL.

- 2 -

DEPARTMENT OF TRANSPORTATION
Federal Aviation Administration

VFR PILOT EXAM-O-GRAM° NO. 47

GROUND EFFECT

It is possible to fly an aircraft a few feet above the ground at an airspeed lower than that required to sustain level flight at an altitude only slightly higher. This is the result of a phenomenon called ground effect -- apparently better known than understood by many pilots. In terms as nontechnical as possible, we will here define and discuss the major problems associated with this rather complex subject.

WHAT IS GROUND EFFECT? It is not possible, nor would it serve our purpose, to attempt in the space available an indepth discussion of the precise aerodynamics of ground effect. Suffice it to say, that in simple terms, it is the result of interaction between wing airflow patterns and the surface of the earth. All airfoils such as wings, rotor blades, etc., produce tip vortices and exhibit distinct airstream downwash characteristics when developing lift. The vertical components of such tip vortices and downwash velocities are progressively reduced as the airfoil nears the surface, and at touchdown are almost completely canceled by surface interference. This alteration in airflow pattern decreases induced drag (the drag produced by lift). The closer the airfoil to the surface, the greater the reduction. Induced drag, at a height of approximately one-tenth of a wing span above the surface, may be 47% less than when the airplane is operating out of ground effect. It is this decrease in drag which explains basic airplane reactions when in ground effect.

HOW DOES A REDUCTION IN INDUCED DRAG AFFECT PERFORMANCE? To the pilot the reduction in drag means increased performance. That is, lift will increase with no increase in angle of attack, or the same lift can be obtained at a smaller angle of attack. This can be useful since it allows the pilot to either decrease angle of attack/power to maintain level flight, or as on most landings, to maintain wing lift while reducing power. A word of caution is in order, however. A full stall landing will require several more degrees of up elevator deflection than would a full stall when done free of ground effect. This is true because ground effect usually changes horizontal tail effectiveness in airplanes of conventional configuration.

UP TO WHAT ALTITUDE CAN GROUND EFFECT BE DETECTED? A pilot is unlikely to detect ground effect if his height above the surface exceeds the airplane's wing span. In fact, there is appreciable ground effect only if height is less than half the wing span. At this or lower altitudes, ground effect is quite pronounced.

WHAT MAJOR PROBLEMS CAN BE CAUSED BY GROUND EFFECT? Floating during landing is, in part, a result of ground effect. An airplane will continue to remain airborne just above the surface at a speed which would have produced an immediate stall had the airplane been a bit higher. Therefore, a pilot may run out of both runway and options if he carries excess speed in the approach, or does not allow for at least a small margin of float after the flare from a normal approach.

Another and perhaps more serious problem, can develop during takeoff and climb out, especially when using a runway of marginal length. Deluded into believing that he has climb-out capability simply because he was able to get in the air, a pilot may raise the gear the instant he is airborne or initiate an immediate climb. For a few feet, all may go well but he may really have only marginal climb performance even in ground effect, and therefore, an acute need for added thrust as he begins to move out of ground effect. Moving out of ground effect, even if it only slightly increases the effectiveness of the elevators, the nose will usually tend to pitch up. At the resultant high angle of attack, the pilot finds he cannot climb, or even worse, may begin to sink. Desperately holding his nose-high attitude in a futile effort to gain altitude, he steadily mushes or stalls back to the runway or into obstructions if no excess power is available to correct the situation. Add high gross weight and density altitude and a bit of turbulence to this scene and an accident is even more likely.

Airspeed indicator unreliability in ground effect is another though less critical problem. Usually it will indicate slightly higher as you leave and slightly lower as you enter ground effect.

Just remember, ground effect is always there; it may prolong the glide or permit an aircraft to get airborne with insufficient power to sustain flight outside the area of ground effect. If this occurs the pilot must allow the airplane to accelerate while still in ground effect, before attempting to continue the climb. Panic attempts to force a climb can only make lift/climb problems worse.

MIDAIR COLLISIONS (Series #3)

| JET ON ROTATION | 15 SECONDS LATER | 60 SECONDS AFTER TAKEOFF AND PASSING THROUGH 2,000' A G L |

Compliance with Flight Rules prescribed in FAR Part 91 and adherence to Good Operating Practices listed in the Airman's Information Manual, will materially reduce the possibility of pilots becoming involved in mid-air collisions. General Aviation Written Tests contain test items on FARs that are related to mid-air collisions. Unfortunately, too many pilots look upon the FARs merely as a dis-agreeable requirement for passing a written test and do not associate FARs with their everyday flying.

In 1968, 2,230 incidents were reported under the FAA "Near Midair Collision Study Program." Of these, 1,128 were "Hazardous" in that the aircraft missed only by chance or after one or both pilots took evasive action. The present phenomenal growth in number of aircraft and hours flown in U.S. Civil Aviation, is rapidly increasing the midair collision problem.

The National Transportation Safety Board special accident prevention study entitled "Midair Colli-sions in U.S. Civil Aviation - 1968," lists 38 midair collisions involving 76 aircraft. In preparing this Exam-O-Gram, a study was made of 31 of the General Aviation accident reports of midair collisions that occurred in 1968 and 23 reports of midairs which occurred prior to October in 1969.

This Exam-O-Gram attempts to show pictorially, where and how some midairs have occurred, as well as other places where the midair hazard may strike again. All pilots should become aware of and exercise every precaution against, the midair collision potentials at controlled high density ter-minal arrival and departure areas. The photographs above show how rapidly a jet on takeoff can become a real hazard to another airplane cruising at 2,000 feet above the ground near a busy airport.

○ ○ ○

WHAT COLLISION PRECAUTIONS SHOULD YOU TAKE FOR CROSS-COUNTRY FLIGHTS? In preflight planning, check Flight Information Publications pertaining to Special Operations, Parachute Jumping Areas, Graphic Notices and the aeronautical charts to determine if the proposed route passes through a Restricted Area, Military Training Route, Terminal Radar Service Area, etc.

Have any fatal mid-airs happened as depicted in the illustra-tion to the right? <u>The answer is YES</u>!

Even though the formation of jets is in a steep climb, they are climbing at 365 knots IAS (420 mph).

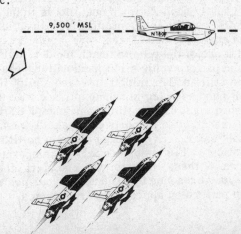

- **HEAVY TRAFFIC AROUND MILITARY FIELDS**

Pilots are advised to exercise vigilance when in close prox-imity to most military airports. These airports may have jet aircraft traffic patterns extending up to 2500 feet above the surface. In addition, they may have an unusually heavy concentration of jet aircraft operating within a 25 nautical mile radius and from the surface to all altitudes. This pre-cautionary note also applies to the larger civil airports.

FLYING NEAR A MILITARY AIRFIELD.

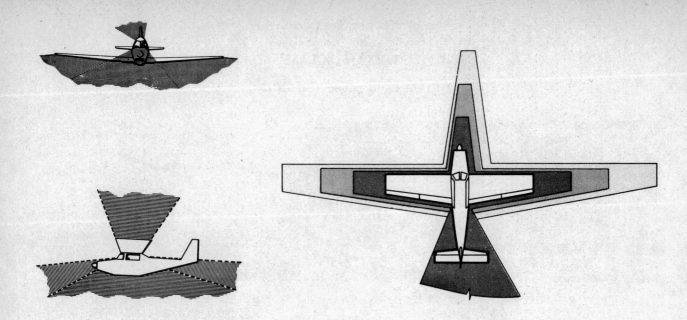

THE BLIND SPOTS WIDEN AND EXTEND TO INFINITY AS SHOWN ABOVE

NOTE: When turning a high-wing airplane the pilot lowers the wing and thus hides the area into which he is turning. In a low-wing airplane, the cabin roof hides the area into which the pilot is turning-- especially in right turns.

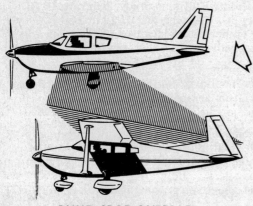

BLIND SPOT OVERLAP

Pilots of high-wing and low-wing airplanes can be in each other's blind spots. Collisions of this type have happened most frequently in the traffic patterns at uncontrolled airports. Collisions like this can occur: (a) on the entry leg of the pattern when the low-wing airplane descends on top of the other airplane; (b) on the downwind leg of the pattern with one of the airplanes flying at an improper pattern altitude--that is, the high-wing airplane climbs or the low-wing airplane descends to return to the desired altitude; (c) on final approach or just before touchdown.

When there is a slower airplane ahead of you in the pattern flying about 100 feet lower than your altitude, it is possible to overtake and never see the slower airplane hidden beneath the nose of your aircraft. Remember, the silhouette of an airplane below the horizon tends to blend with, and be lost in, the surrounding landscape features.

WHEN HAS THIS TYPE COLLISION OCCURRED? It usually happens when one pilot is flying the traffic pattern in an unauthorized direction. Of the cases studied, there were 3 midairs involved with one of the pilots in each incident flying a right hand pattern while a left hand pattern was in use-- and still another midair involved a pilot flying a left hand base leg in noncompliance with the published right hand traffic. The use of UNICOM at uncontrolled airports can make flying around them safer. Even though there is no UNICOM station or Flight Service Station in operation at some of these airports, you can alert other pilots of your presence by announcing your position in the pattern on appropriate frequencies.

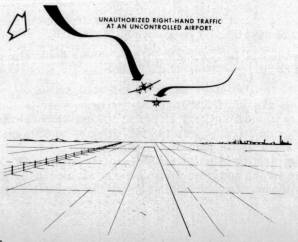

UNAUTHORIZED RIGHT-HAND TRAFFIC AT AN UNCONTROLLED AIRPORT.

Of the accident reports studied, there were 8 midairs elsewhere in the pattern (entry, exit, downwind, etc.). One fatal accident occurred when a student and his instructor in a light aircraft were leaving the pattern and collided with a multi-engine aircraft on the downwind leg (as represented by airplanes B and C).

This illustration also shows how an airplane making a pattern entry to the downwind leg could collide head-on with another airplane that has flown a <u>long crosswind leg before making the exit turn.</u> (See airplanes A and C).

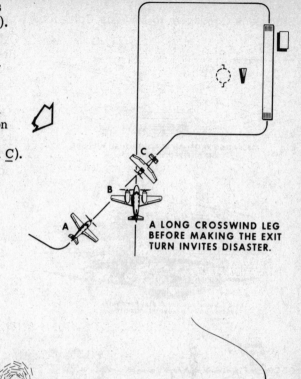

A LONG CROSSWIND LEG BEFORE MAKING THE EXIT TURN INVITES DISASTER.

<u>X</u> MARKS THE SPOT

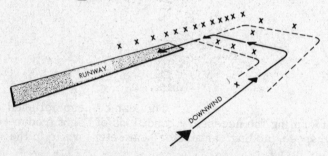

APPROXIMATE POSITION OF MID-AIR COLLISIONS THAT OCCURED DURING 1968 IN THE DOWN-WIND, BASE-LEG AND FINAL APPROACH.

o o o

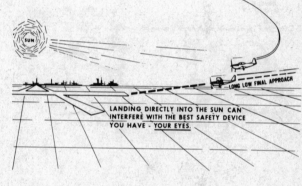

LANDING DIRECTLY INTO THE SUN CAN INTERFERE WITH THE BEST SAFETY DEVICE YOU HAVE - YOUR EYES.

OTHER ACTUAL MIDAIRS

1- Two solo students departed on the same cross-country flight and ran together while looking at their charts.
2- One airplane descended on top of a white colored airplane which blended with the snow covered terrain.

SOME FEDERAL AVIATION REGULATIONS RELATED TO MIDAIR COLLISIONS WITH WHICH PILOTS SHOULD BE THOROUGHLY FAMILIAR AND ADHERE TO, INCLUDE: 91.9, Careless and Reckless Operation; 91.11, Liquor and Drugs; 91.65, Operating Near Other Aircraft; 91.67, Right-of-Way Rules; 91.70, Aircraft Speed; 91.87, Operation at Airports with Operating Control Towers; 91.89, Operation at Airports Without Control Towers; and 91.79, General Limitations.

• • • •

SITUATIONS CONDUCIVE TO MIDAIR COLLISIONS

Constant vigilance is a <u>must</u> when practicing pylon 8's, low level ground track maneuvers like "turns about a point," or "S turns across a road."

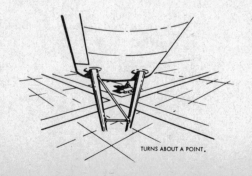

TURNS ABOUT A POINT.

HOW SAFE ARE YOU WITH A SLEEPY SAFETY PILOT ?

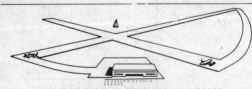

OPERATING FROM AN UNCONTROLLED AIRPORT
ON DIFFERENT RUNWAYS.

ARE CLEARING PROCEDURES HELPFUL IN REDUC-
ING AIRCRAFT COLLISION POTENTIAL? Yes, pilots
should execute gentle banks, left and right, when climbing or descending, rather than spending long periods of
time climbing and descending straight ahead. The AIM
Good Operating Procedures state in part: "Appropriate
clearing procedures should precede the execution of all
turns including chandelles, lazy eights, stalls, slow
flight, climbs, straight-and-level, spins, and other
combination maneuvers."

CLOSED CURTAINS ARE NICE FOR THE PASSENGERS,
BUT THEY DON'T IMPROVE THE VISIBILITY.

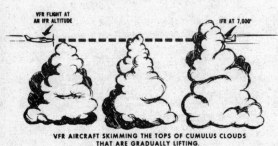

VFR AIRCRAFT SKIMMING THE TOPS OF CUMULUS CLOUDS
THAT ARE GRADUALLY LIFTING.

This can be accomplished
by performing the necessary conditions of flight (reducing airspeed, adding carburetor heat, etc.) while in the
clearing turns.

For several decades military flying schools have taught
their pilots to perform at least one 180° clearing turn
in each direction before entering such maneuvers as
spins, Cuban 8's, Immelmans, etc., where considerable altitude changes are involved.

-4-

USE OF OXYGEN IN GENERAL AVIATION AIRCRAFT

EACH OCCUPANT OF THE AIRCRAFT MUST BE PROVIDED WITH SUPPLEMENTAL OXYGEN
AT CABIN PRESSURE ALTITUDES ABOVE 15,000 FT. MSL

REQUIRED MINIMUM FLIGHT CREW MUST USE SUPPLEMENTAL OXYGEN DURING THE ENTIRE FLIGHT TIME
AT CABIN PRESSURE ALTITUDES ABOVE 14,000 FT. MSL

REQUIRED MINIMUM FLIGHT CREW MUST USE SUPPLEMENTAL OXYGEN FOR THAT PART OF THE FLIGHT THAT IS OF MORE THAN 30 MINUTES DURATION
AT CABIN PRESSURE ALTITUDES ABOVE 12,500 FT. MSL

Continuing increases both in the number of high-performance and light turbocharged general aviation aircraft and the number of aircraft concentrated in lower altitudes, encourage more pilots to get out of the "physiological zone" (sea level to 12,000 ft.) into the "physiological deficient zone" (12,000 to 50,000 ft.) as a matter of economy and safety. In the lower zone, only minor oxygen problems exist. However, in the higher zone, oxygen deficiency can result in a pilot or passenger becoming a severe hypoxic case.

WHAT IS HYPOXIA? Hypoxia is the result of a lack of sufficient oxygen in the body cells or tissues. There are several types of hypoxia but this Exam-O-Gram discusses only the hypoxic type or altitude hypoxia -- that occurs in the "physiological deficient" zone.

WHAT ARE HAZARDS OF HYPOXIA? The most important single hazard characteristic of hypoxia at altitude is that if the pilot becomes too engrossed with his flight duties, he may not notice the symptoms or effects of hypoxia. For example: A pilot, flying at 24,000 feet in an unpressurized aircraft, inadvertently pulls his mask connector out of the oxygen system outlet. Engrossed with radio communications and flying "instruments," he fails to notice the separation. At this altitude, without supplemental oxygen, his time of useful consciousness (amount of time a pilot is able to effectively or adequately fly his aircraft with an insufficient supply of oxygen) is 3 minutes. Beyond this he will probably be unable to recognize his problem or do anything about it.
At flight altitudes, above 12,000 ft., the onset of hypoxia is insidious. All persons begin to deteriorate in alertness and mental efficiency to some degree above 12,000 ft. without supplemental oxygen. Above 14,000 ft., distinct impairment of mental functions occurs--especially with respect to mathematical and reasoning capabilities.

WHAT ARE SYMPTOMS OF HYPOXIA? Since individuals differ widely in their reaction to hypoxia, it is impossible to group symptoms in a specific order. Therefore, in order to detect hypoxia, you need to know your own symptoms from the following list: (1) Increased breathing rate, headache, fatigue; (2) light headed or dizzy sensations, listlessness; (3) tingling or warm sensations, sweating; (4) poor coordination, impairment of judgment; (5) loss of, or reduced vision, sleepiness; (6) blue coloring of skin, fingernails, and lips; and (7) behavior changes, a feeling of well being (euphoria).

IS VISION AFFECTED BY LACK OF OXYGEN? The cellular retina of the eye is highly susceptible to lack of oxygen. Since rod cells are several hundred percent more sensitive to lack of oxygen than cone cells, night vision is sharply impaired at higher altitudes -- even though other symptoms of hypoxia may not be apparent. It is said that a pilot flying at night is 24 % blind at 8,000 ft.; 50% blind at 12,000 ft. This is why supplemental oxygen is recommended when flying above 5,000 ft. at night.

AT WHAT ALTITUDE ARE YOU LIKELY TO GET HYPOXIA? Anyone flying above 12,000 ft. in an unpressurized aircraft without supplemental oxygen is a potential hypoxia case. However, there is a wide, individual variation in susceptibility to hypoxia. Physical fitness and other factors (alcohol, drugs, tobacco, etc.) may change your ability to tolerate hypoxia even from day to day. (If the smoke of 3 cigarettes is inhaled at sea level, a person's visual acuity and dark adaptation are reduced to the extent of mild hypoxia encountered in flight at 8,000 ft. Smoking at 10,000 ft. produces effects equivalent to those experienced at 14,000 ft. without smoking.) NOTE: 10,000 ft. is a good operational practice "physiological zone" upper limit.

HOW CAN HYPOXIA BE PREVENTED? By flying at altitudes below 12,000 ft.; by flying in pressurized aircraft; or by breathing supplemental oxygen when above 12,000 ft. in unpressurized aircraft.

HOW IS OXYGEN STORED IN THE AIRCRAFT? It is stored in metal cylinders generally attached to the aircraft, outside of the cabin area -- e.g., in the baggage area. However, portable systems are often used, in which case, the cylinder would normally be stored in the cockpit or cabin and should be securely anchored. In a high-pressure system, oxygen is stored at a pressure of 1800 psi.; in a low-pressure system at 450 psi. General aviation and airlines use the high-pressure system extensively. The low-pressure system is used primarily by the military.

CAN THE TWO PRESSURE SYSTEMS BE EASILY DIFFERENTIATED? Military services have a color-coding system, civilian industry does not. In the military, high-pressure cylinders are green; low-pressure cylinders, yellow. In civilian industry cylinders may be any color. Know the pressure-capacity of your oxygen cylinder. A castastrophic disintegration may occur if someone attempts to fill a low-pressure cylinder to a pressure of 1800 psi.

CAN ANY KIND OF OXYGEN BE USED FOR AVIATOR'S BREATHING OXYGEN? No! Oxygen used for medical purposes or welding normally should not be used because it may contain too much water. The excess water could condense and freeze in oxygen lines when flying at high altitudes. This could block oxygen flow. Also, constant use of oxygen containing too much water may cause corrosion in the system. Specifications for "aviators breathing oxygen" are 99.5% pure oxygen and not more than .005 mg. of water per liter of oxygen. So, always ask for "aviators breathing oxygen."

HOW CAN YOU DETERMINE IF OXYGEN SERVICE IS AVAILABLE AT AN AIRPORT? The Airport/Facility Directory includes this information in the airport data. The upper illustration to the left is excerpted from the airport data for Addison Airport. The lower illustration is an excerpt from the directory legend. The arrows point out that both "high pressure" and "low pressure" bottles can be serviced with oxygen at Addison Airport in Dallas, Texas. Since the numbers "3" and "4" do not appear after the "OX" in the airport data, replacement bottles are not available.

DALLAS
§ **ADDISON** (ADS) 8.7 N GMT-6(-5DT) 32°58'06''N 96°50'11''W
   643 B S4 **FUEL** 100, JET A1 + OX 1, 2
   RWY 15-33: H7199X100 (ASPH) S-80, D-160 MIRL Centerline reflectors only
   RWY 15: MALSR. Thld dsplcd 990'. **RWY 33:** REIL. Pole 60' from thld.

OXYGEN
OX 1 High Pressure
OX 2 Low Pressure
OX 3 High Pressure—Replacement Bottles
OX 4 Low Pressure—Replacement Bottles

WHAT ARE THE 3 TYPES OF OXYGEN BREATHING SYSTEMS NORMALLY USED? Continuous Flow -- used up to 25,000 ft.; Demand -- used up to 35,000 ft.; and Pressure Demand -- used up to 45,000 ft. Most general aviation aircraft use the Continuous-Flow type. The more sophisticated general aviation aircraft ("bizjets," etc.) have the Pressure-Demand type for crew members because of the altitudes at which they are flown, but a Continuous-Flow type is generally used for passengers, as the masks are simpler to don and passengers do not require as much oxygen as the pilot.

HOW DOES A CONTINUOUS-FLOW OXYGEN SYSTEM OPERATE? It is usually characterized by the bag attached to the mask. Oxygen is constantly dispensed from the oxygen storage bottle through the regulating system to the bag and mask. As the wearer inhales the oxygen from the "rebreather" bag, it deflates; as he exhales, some of the unused oxygen is forced back into the bag and mixed with 100% oxygen for the next inhalation. Some is forced out through a cluster of small orifices either in the nose of the mask or on either side. To check for oxygen flow, there is usually a mechanical oxygen flow indicator (of some color) in the tubing leading to the rebreather bag. If, when you inhale, the colored indicator disappears behind a small opaque section of the tube, oxygen is flowing. Another way of checking for flow is to pinch off the tube between the mask and the point at which oxygen enters the bag. If the bag inflates, oxygen is flowing. Remember, just because you can breathe does not mean that oxygen is flowing. Even though oxygen is not flowing, you could still breathe through the cluster of holes in the mask, but you would only be getting cabin air.

HOW IS OXYGEN-FLOW RATE CONTROLLED IN CONTINUOUS-FLOW TYPE SYSTEMS? By fixed orifices or packing, manually, or fully automatic. In those controlled by a fixed orifice or packing, the orifices for the pilot and crew members are larger or the packing is less dense than for passengers because pilot and crew members are more active and, therefore, need more oxygen. In the manually-controlled type, a knob on the regulator may be adjusted to the flight altitude. The higher the altitude to which the regulator is set, the greater the flow rate. In fully automatic types, an altitude-sensing device changes flow rate automatically as the aircraft climbs or descends. For those systems in which packing is used to control flow-rate, one must be sure that the plug-in and the outlet into which it is plugged are compatible. Why? Because one company may put the packing in the plug-in and another may put the packing in the outlet. If you use a plug-in with the packing, in an outlet with the packing, you may totally cut off the flow of oxygen. Conversely, if you use a plug-in with no packing, in an outlet with no packing, flow-rate would be too great and the oxygen would be depleted in a short time. Generally, the only way you can join non-compatible units is by forcing the plug-in into the receptacle. Don't do this! If it doesn't insert easily, check for non-compatibility.

HOW DOES A DEMAND OXYGEN SYSTEM OPERATE? This system furnishes oxygen to the user

 only when he demands it -- that is, when he inhales. A small lever adjustment enables the pilot to select either of 2 settings, "normal oxygen" or "100% oxygen." The amount of oxygen received depends upon the flight altitude. As altitude is increased, the amount of cabin air is automatically decreased and the amount of oxygen is automatically increased. Most demand regulators are designed to give 100% oxygen by the time 30,000 ft. is attained. With the "100% oxygen" setting, the user receives 100% oxygen at all altitudes. The mask used for this system is designed to give an air-tight and oxygen-tight seal for the face. This system can be used safely to 35,000 ft.

HOW DOES A PRESSURE-DEMAND OXYGEN SYSTEM OPERATE? This system operates in exactly

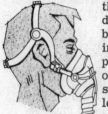 the same way as the "demand" system except that, at higher altitudes, oxygen is delivered under positive pressure to the face mask. Positive oxygen pressure can be automatically or manually activated at approximately 30,000 ft. and automatically increases as altitude increases. Positive pressure is needed in order to maintain proper lung oxygen pressure, and blood oxygen saturation during flight to altitudes of 35,000 to 45,000 ft. in an unpressurized aircraft. In this system it is essential that the mask be adjusted to obtain a leak-proof seal to the face. Inhaling is effortless but, because of the positive pressure, conscious effort must be exerted to exhale, and one may find it difficult to talk.

WHAT IS A PRESSURIZED AIRCRAFT? It is an aircraft in which pressure in the cockpit and passenger compartment is maintained at an altitude lower than the actual flight altitude by compressing air into these areas.

WHAT IS MEANT BY DECOMPRESSION? Decompression is the inability of the aircraft's pressurization system to maintain the designed "aircraft cabin" pressure. For example, an aircraft is flying at an altitude of 29,000 feet but the aircraft cabin is pressurized to an altitude equivalent to 8,500 ft. If decompression occurs, the cabin pressure may become equivalent to that of the aircraft's altitude of 29,000 ft. The rate at which this occurs depends on the severity of decompression. This could be caused by a malfunction in the pressurization system or by structural damage to the aircraft. There are two kinds of decompression:

EXPLOSIVE DECOMPRESSION - Cabin pressure decreases faster than the lungs can decompress. Most authorities consider that any decompression which occurs in less than 1/2 second as explosive and potentially dangerous. This type could only be caused by structural damage, material failure, or by a door "popping" open.

RAPID DECOMPRESSION - A change in cabin pressure when the lungs decompress faster than the cabin. There is no likelihood of lung damage in this case. This type could be caused by a failure or malfunction in the pressurization system itself, or through slow leaks in the pressurized area.

WHAT ARE THE DANGERS OF DECOMPRESSION? The primary danger is hypoxia, but some cases of bends have occurred. If oxygen equipment is not used properly above 30,000 ft., unconsciousness will occur in a very short time. The average time of useful consciousness without oxygen is 30 seconds. This is why the oxygen mask should be worn when flying at high altitudes--35,000 ft. or higher, and ready for immediate donning at lower altitudes. Crew members should select the 100% oxygen setting on their oxygen regulator at high altitude if the aircraft is equipped with a demand or pressure-demand oxygen system.

WHAT ARE SOME GENERAL RULES FOR OXYGEN SAFETY? (1) Do not inspect oxygen equipment with greasy hands or permit an accumulation of oily waste or residue in the vicinity of the oxygen system (the combination of grease and 100% gaseous oxygen creates an explosive situation); (2) do not use "military-surplus" oxygen equipment unless it is inspected by a certified FAA-inspection station and approved for use; (3) do not smoke or permit smoking or ignite any flame while the oxygen system is being used; (4) do not place a portable oxygen container in an aircraft unless it is securely fastened to prevent movement or displacement in case of turbulence, unusual attitudes, etc. ; (5) utilize a check list to check your oxygen system for condition and proper operation prior to taking off on any flight during which you might need oxygen; and (6) brief your passengers on the proper use of the oxygen equipment. This is extremely important in case of an emergency in larger general aviation pressurized aircraft in which the cockpit and passenger compartments are separate. Passengers should know what to expect, what to do, and how to use the equipment. Use the check-list recommended for your equipment. If factory installed, you should find it in the Airplane Flight Manual or Owner's Manual.

IS THERE ANY PLACE WHERE CIVILIAN PILOTS CAN OBTAIN PHYSIOLOGICAL TRAINING? Yes! The Aeromedical Education Branch of the FAA's Civil Aeromedical Institute (CAMI) in Oklahoma City, Oklahoma, gives one-day physiological training courses -- including an altitude chamber flight in which you would get a chance to see what your hypoxia symptoms are. This training is open to the aviation public and courses are given on a "demand" basis as funds are available. This course is also given to civilian pilots under FAA sponsorship at various Air Force Bases across the country. For further information write to: Civil Aeromedical Institute, Attention: Aeromedical Education Branch, AC-140, P. O. Box 25082 - 6500 South MacArthur, Oklahoma City, Oklahoma 73125.

DO FARs REQUIRE THAT GENERAL AVIATION AIRCRAFT HAVE OXYGEN ABOARD? Yes! FAR 91.32 requires that the required minimum flight crew, for all aircraft operating at cabin pressure altitudes above 12,500 ft. MSL up to and including 14,000 ft. MSL, be provided with and use supplemental oxygen for any part of the flight of more than 30 min. duration at these altitudes; above 14,000 ft. MSL, the required minimum flight crew is required to use supplemental oxygen during the entire flight time at these altitudes; and above 15,000 ft. MSL, each occupant must be provided with supplemental oxygen. Additional rules are specified for pressurized aircraft.

- 4 -

INTERPRETING SECTIONAL CHARTS (SERIES 3)

SPECIAL USE AIRSPACE

This is the third in a series of Exam-O-Grams dealing with understanding and interpreting aeronautical symbols and legends of the new-type Sectional Charts. See VFR Exam-O-Grams Nos. 23 and 50.

FAR, Part 73.3, states in part: "Special Use Airspace consists of airspace of defined dimensions identified by an area on the surface of the earth wherein activities must be confined because of their nature, or wherein limitations are imposed upon aircraft operations that are not a part of those activities, or both." Special Use Airspace depicted on aeronautical charts are: Prohibited Areas, Restricted Areas, Warning Areas, Alert Areas, and Military Operations Areas (MOA). These areas are depicted on the charts in many shapes and sizes and their boundaries are outlined by crosshatching like this ⟶ ▨▨▨▨ .

In addition, supplemental information about Prohibited, Restricted, Warning, and Alert Areas is printed on the border of the charts like this.

▪▪▪▪▪▪▪▪▪

PROHIBITED, RESTRICTED, WARNING, AND ALERT AREAS ON ATLANTA SECTIONAL CHART

NO.	NAME	ALTITUDE	TIME	APPROPRIATE AUTHORITY
P-77	Plains, Ga.	To 1500	Continuous	Admin., FAA, Washington, D.C.
R-2101	Anniston Army Depot, Ala.	To 5000	0700 to 1800 Mon. thru Fri.	Anniston Army Depot
W-497	Patrick AFB, Fla	Unlimi...	...inuous	Comdr., AF Eastern Test Range, Patrick AFB, Fla.
A-291B	Miami, Fla.		Sunrise to sunset daily.	All Local Flying Schools & Flying Clubs Greater Miami Area.

EXCERPTS

P - Prohibited   R - Restricted   W - Warning   A - Alert   † - Controlling Agency

Unless otherwise noted: Altitudes are MSL and in feet; time is local.

No person shall operate an aircraft within a Prohibited Area, or within a Restricted Area between the designated altitudes during the time of designation unless prior permission has been issued by the appropriate authority as listed above. The appropriate authority is defined as either the controlling agency (†) or the using agency.

Flight within Alert Areas is not restricted, but pilots are advised to exercise extreme caution.

WHAT IS A PROHIBITED AREA? It is designated airspace within which the flight of aircraft is not allowed for security or other reasons associated with national welfare. An example of a Prohibited Area is the area that encompasses the White House and the Capitol buildings in Washington, D. C. It is designated P-56 and extends from the surface to flight level 180. AVOID THIS AREA! Three Prohibited Areas (designated P-204, P-205, and P-206) are located southeast of International Falls, Minnesota. These Prohibited Areas were established to safeguard the forest and wildlife in one of the few remaining wilderness areas in the United States. They extend from the surface to 4,000 feet. AVOID THESE AREAS!

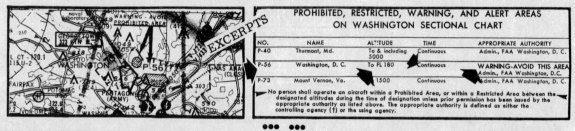

PROHIBITED, RESTRICTED, WARNING, AND ALERT AREAS ON WASHINGTON SECTIONAL CHART

NO.	NAME	ALTITUDE	TIME	APPROPRIATE AUTHORITY
P-40	Thurmont, Md.	To & including 5000	Continuous	Admin., FAA Washington, D. C.
P-56	Washington, D. C.	To FL 180	Continuous	WARNING-AVOID THIS AREA Admin., FAA Washington, D. C.
P-73	Mount Vernon, Va.	1500	Continuous	Admin., FAA Washington, D. C.

No person shall operate an aircraft within a Prohibited Area, or within a Restricted Area between the designated altitudes during the time of designation unless prior permission has been issued by the appropriate authority as listed above. The appropriate authority is defined as either the controlling agency (†) or the using agency.

WHAT IS A RESTRICTED AREA? It is designated airspace within which flight, while NOT wholly prohibited, is subject to restrictions. A Restricted Area is designated when it is determined necessary to confine or segregate activities considered to be hazardous to nonparticipating aircraft. They denote the existence of unusual, often invisible, hazards to aircraft such as artillery firing, aerial gunnery, or guided missiles. Penetration of Restricted Areas without authorization from the using or controlling agency may be extremely hazardous to the aircraft and its occupants. Permission must be received from the appropriate authority to operate an aircraft within a Restricted Area between the designated altitudes during the time specified.

PROHIBITED, RESTRICTED, WARNING, AND ALERT AREAS ON DALLAS-FT WORTH SECTIONAL CHART

NO.	NAME	ALTITUDE	TIME	APPROPRIATE AUTHORITY
R-5601A	Fort Sill, Okla.	To FL 230	Continuous	C. G. Fort Sill, Okla.
R-5601B	Fort Sill, Okla.	To FL 230	Continuous	† FAA, Fort Worth ARTC Center or area FSS. C. G. Fort Sill, Oklahoma

P - Prohibited   R - Restricted   W - Warning   A - Alert   † - Controlling Agency

Unless otherwise noted: Altitudes are MSL and in feet; time is local.

WHAT IS A WARNING AREA? It is airspace, within international airspace, established to contain hazardous operations conducted by U.S. military forces. The activities conducted within Warning Areas may be as hazardous to nonparticipating aircraft and its occupants as those contained within Restricted Areas. However, NO restriction to flight is imposed because flight within international airspace cannot legally be restricted. To alert nonparticipants to the existence of possible hazardous conditions, Warning Areas are depicted on aeronautical charts. Most Warning Areas lie within 3 statute miles of a coast line. When flying along an uneven coast line, shortcuts over water could result in unintentional flight into a Warning Area. BE ALERT and refer to the appropriate chart when flying along any coastline.

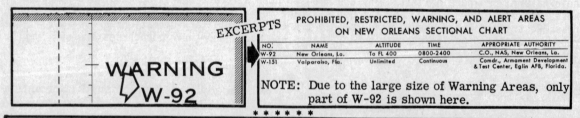

PROHIBITED, RESTRICTED, WARNING, AND ALERT AREAS ON NEW ORLEANS SECTIONAL CHART

NO.	NAME	ALTITUDE	TIME	APPROPRIATE AUTHORITY
W-92	New Orleans, La.	To FL 400	0800-2400	C.O., NAS, New Orleans, La.
W-151	Valparaiso, Fla.	Unlimited	Continuous	Comdr., Armament Development & Test Center, Eglin AFB, Florida.

NOTE: Due to the large size of Warning Areas, only part of W-92 is shown here.

It is always the responsibility of the PILOT of any aircraft to do his best to avoid a collision when operating in VFR conditions, regardless of the type of operation being conducted, the area being used, or the type flight plan filed. Three Exam-O-Grams were written to help educate pilots in the ART OF COLLISION AVOIDANCE. It is certainly appropriate to mention them when writing about the rules governing Special Use Airspace. Review VFR Exam-O-Grams Nos. 22, 29, and 48.

WHAT IS AN ALERT AREA? It is designated airspace which may contain a high volume of pilot training activities or an unusual type of aeronautical activity--neither of which is hazardous to aircraft. Alert Areas are depicted on aeronautical charts to alert pilots of nonparticipating aircraft of the activity within a specific area. All activity within an Alert Area shall be conducted in accordance with Federal Aviation Regulations, without waiver, and pilots of participating aircraft as well as pilots of aircraft transiting the area, shall be equally responsible for collision avoidance. The establishment of Alert Areas does not impose any flight restrictions or communication requirements on any pilots, although Flight Service Stations in the vicinity may broadcast information regarding the use being made of the area as circumstances dictate.

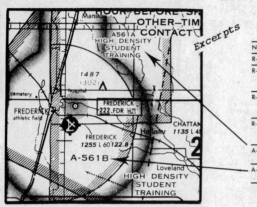

Excerpts

PROHIBITED, RESTRICTED, WARNING, AND ALERT AREAS
ON DALLAS-FT WORTH SECTIONAL CHART

NO.	NAME	ALTITUDE	TIME	APPROPRIATE AUTHORITY
R-5601A	Fort Sill, Okla.	To 23,000	Continuous	C. G., Fort Sill, Okla.
R-5601B	Fort Sill, Okla.	To 23,000	Continuous	† FAA, Fort Worth ARTC Center or area FSS. C. G., Fort Sill, Oklahoma
R-5601D	Fort Sill, Okla.	To 16,500	Sunrise to sunset	† FAA, Fort Worth ARTC Center or area FSS. C. G., Fort Sill, Oklahoma
R-5601E	Fort Sill, Okla.	To 6000	Sunrise to sunset	† FAA, Fort Worth ARTC Center or area FSS. C. G., Fort Sill, Okla.
A-561A	Frederick, Okla.	3000 to & incl 4200	0700-2300 Mon-Fri	Comdr. Sheppard AFB, Texas
A-561B	Frederick, Okla.	To & incl 3200	0700-2300 Mon-Fri	Comdr. Sheppard AFB, Texas

† Flight within Alert Areas is not restricted, but pilots are advised to exercise extreme caution.

● ● ●

WHAT ARE MILITARY OPERATIONS AREAS (MOAs)? Military Operations Areas consist of airspace of defined vertical and lateral limits established for the purpose of separating certain military training activities from IFR traffic. Whenever an MOA is being used, nonparticipating IFR traffic may be cleared through an MOA if IFR separation can be provided by ATC. Otherwise, ATC will reroute or restrict nonparticipating IFR traffic.

Some training activities may necessitate acrobatic maneuvers, and the USAF is exempted from the regulation prohibiting acrobatic flight on airways within MOAs.

Pilots operating under VFR should exercise extreme caution while flying within an MOA when military activity is being conducted. Information regarding activity in MOA's may be obtained from any FSS within 200 miles of the area.

These areas will be depicted on Sectional, VFR Terminal, and Low Altitude En Route Charts.

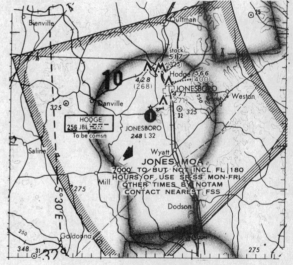

* * * * * * * *

WHO CAN AUTHORIZE THE OPERATION OF AN AIRCRAFT IN SPECIAL USE AIRSPACE? An Appropriate Authority, defined as either the Using Agency or the Controlling Agency, may authorize transit through, or flight within, Special Use Airspace.

The Using Agency is the agency, organization, or military command whose activity within a Restricted Area necessitated the area being so designated, or that established the requirement for the Prohibited Area.

The Controlling Agency is the FAA facility that may authorize the transit through, or flight within, a Restricted Area in accordance with a joint-use letter issued under FAR Part 73.15.

Contact the Using Agency for Warning Area and Alert Area information.

● ● ● ●

ALTHOUGH NOT CLASSIFIED AS A SPECIAL USE AIRSPACE, THERE ARE OTHER AREAS THAT HAVE LIMITATIONS TO FLIGHT AS REGULATED BY THE SERVICE THAT ADMINISTERS THEM.

The excerpt to the right shows how National Wildlife Refuges are depicted on a sectional chart.

☆ ☆ ☆

In the margin of the sectional charts, information is listed concerning flight over National Park Service Areas, U.S. Fish and Wildlife Service Areas, and U.S. Forest Services Areas as shown below:

REGULATIONS REGARDING FLIGHTS OVER CHARTED NATIONAL PARK SERVICE AREAS, U.S. FISH AND WILDLIFE SERVICE AREAS, AND U.S. FOREST SERVICE AREAS

EXCERPT

The landing of aircraft is prohibited on lands or waters administered by the National Park Service, U.S. Fish and Wildlife Service or U.S. Forest Service without authorization from the respective agency. Exceptions include: 1) when forced to land due to an emergency beyond the control of the operator, 2) at officially designated landing sites, or 3) on approved official business of the Federal Government.

All aircraft are requested to maintain a minimum altitude of 2,000 feet above the terrain of the following: National Parks, Monuments, Seashores, Lakeshores, Recreation Areas and Scenic Riverways administered by the National Park Service; National Wildlife Refuges, Big Game Refuges, Game Ranges and Wildlife Ranges administered by the U.S. Fish and Wildlife Service; and Wilderness and Primitive areas administered by the U.S. Forest Service.

Federal regulations also prohibit airdrops by parachute or other means of persons, cargo or objects from aircraft on lands administered by the three agencies without authorization from the respective agency. Exceptions include: 1) emergencies involving the safety of human life or 2) threat of serious property loss.

 Boundary of National Park Service areas, U.S. Fish and Wildlife Service areas and U.S. Forest Service Wilderness and Primitive areas.

☆ ☆ ☆ ☆ ☆

This Exam-O-Gram emphasizes the study and use of information printed on sectional charts. Study the borders and legend of your chart. Know what to look for, what to expect, and what is available to you along your route of flight.

-4-

SKY COVER AND CEILING

A frequently misunderstood portion of the Aviation Weather Report is that part which contains SKY COVER and CEILING information. Do _you_ thoroughly understand the following? TXK 3Ø SCT E5Ø BKN 1ØØ OVC...

The "E5Ø BKN" in the report indicates that the weather observer at TXK _estimated_ the ceiling (broken clouds) to be 5,000 feet above the surface. Although an estimated ceiling is the least reliable of all ceiling reports, it is based on specific guides and is reasonably accurate and operationally useful. If you understand the methods used in making weather observations, you are likely to make better use of available weather reports.

HOW IS SKY COVER DETERMINED? The observer estimates the amount of the total sky that is covered by clouds or obscuring phenomena, and reports this amount of cover in tenths. Two examples of a sky condition which the weather observer would consider as scattered (one-tenth to five-tenths coverage) are shown in figures 1 and 2.

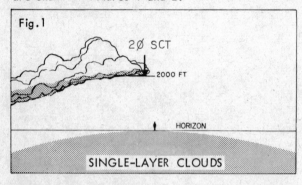

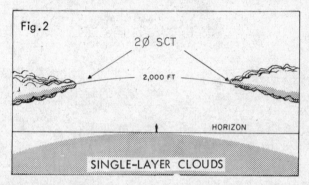

Scattered clouds tend to be of little concern to many pilots. However, the reported scattered clouds could change to either "overcast" or "clear" after the observation was made. Increasing cloud cover, headwinds, dwindling fuel supply, and deteriorating weather could cause problems for the non-instrument rated pilot planning (on the basis of the report) to descend between scattered clouds. Remember, the Aviation Weather Report contains local weather only, at observation time, and is not to be considered a forecast. Your observation in flight is far more timely than a report that must be processed through the communication system. Therefore, when clouds are increasing, _you_ must determine when the time has come to make your descent to avoid getting stranded on top.

The summation principle is applied when two or more cloud layers are present (see figures 3 and 4).

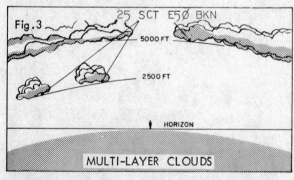

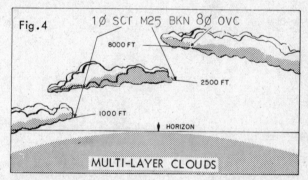

Cloud coverage of six- to nine-tenths of the sky is classified as broken---more than nine-tenths as overcast. However, a report of broken or overcast clouds at a specified height does not necessarily mean that the cloud layer at that altitude actually covers six- to nine-tenths or more than nine-tenths of the sky. The weather observer often does not know the actual extent of the higher cloud layers because his view is restricted by lower cloud layers. Therefore, he uses the summation principle in reporting the amount of sky covered by clouds. In this method, the observer adds the amount of sky covered by the lower clouds to the amount covered by clouds at higher levels. Thus, he reports the amount of sky covered by the combination of lower and higher clouds. A word of caution here--if the weather observer cannot see half or more of the sky above the base of a given cloud layer, most likely you cannot see half or more of the surface when flying above the base of that layer!

HOW IS CLOUD HEIGHT DETERMINED? By using specific guides, the trained observer usually arrives at reasonably accurate estimates (E). The ceiling designator (E) ESTIMATED CEILING--means heights are determined from pilot reports, balloons, or other measurements not meeting criteria for measured ceiling. The ceiling designator (M) MEASURED CEILING--heights determined by ceilometer, ceiling light, cloud detection radar, or by unobscured portion of a landmark protruding into ceiling layer You should trust a report of "measured" ceiling more than one which is "estimated," although either in conjunction with visibility, determines whether VFR conditions exist.

The ceiling designator (W) is spoken as Indefinite Ceiling--vertical visibility into a surface based obstruction. Regardless of method of determination, vertical visibility is classified as an indefinite ceiling.

This Exam-O-Gram should be studied in conjunction with VFR Exam-O-Grams 20, 44, and 46. Together, they should help you understand that surface observations are spot reports; they may not provide the total enroute weather picture at flight time. You must also rely on forecasts and trends, radar weather reports, pilot reports, and your own timely observations in flight.

EMERGENCY LOCATOR TRANSMITTERS (ELTs)

This Exam-O-Gram is issued to help fill the need of those studying for FAA airman written tests and of certificated pilots for additional information concerning the Emergency Locator Transmitter (ELT).

What is an Emergency Locator Transmitter or ELT?

It is a small, self-contained radio transmitter which is activated automatically by the impact force of a crash. It may also be activated manually by an "On-Off" switch. It transmits a distinctive variable tone on the emergency frequencies 121.5 and 243.0 megahertz. The range of an activated ELT varies from 75 to 150 miles, depending on environment. Its useful life varies from 3 to 8 days, depending on battery condition.

Is there a law requiring an ELT in all airplanes?

Yes. Public Law 91-596 was passed by Congress in 1970. As a consequence, FAR 91.52 now requires that an approved ELT must be installed in most U.S. registered airplanes There are certain exceptions to this law; they are: (1) Turbojet airplanes, (2) Agricultural airplanes while dispensing chemicals, (3) Scheduled airline operations not over water or uninhabited areas, (4) Training airplanes operated within 50 miles of point of origin of flight, and (5) Aircraft equipped to carry not more than one person.

What is the purpose of an ELT?

It is designed to transmit an immediate electronic distress signal which can be used by other pilots and search and rescue organizations to locate a downed airplane. The pilot should always determine the ELT's location in the airplane; how to activate it manually; and, if it is portable, how to remove it from the airplane.

How can it be determined if an ELT is approved?

In order to carry out the provision of the law, a Technical Standard Order (TSO C91) has been issued by the FAA which covers the design and operational characteristics of approved locators. A label on the ELT indicates whether the unit meets these standards.

How often must battery be changed?

Battery replacement is required at 50 percent of the normal shelf life as defined by the manufacturer, or after one cumulative hour of use. Under the preventative maintenance provision of FAR 43, this battery replacement may be made by a certificated pilot. For expected reliability and life expectancy only those batteries recommended by the manufacturer should be used. Purchased batteries should be stamped with the date of the 50 percent battery life. The new expiration date for the replacement (or recharged) battery must be legibly marked on the outside of the transmitter. Failure to replace batteries at the specified dates may not only limit the operating time but may cause some damaging corrosion within the unit.

How can premature battery deterioration be minimized?

Premature battery deterioration can be minimized by preventing exposure to high temperature such as might be experienced in an aircraft parked on a ramp, or to extremely low temperatures. Anything that a pilot can do in time of emergency to obtain a battery temperature of approximately 70° will result in improved performance and longer operation of the ELT.

How can the pilot check ELT operation?

Operational testing can be done by tuning the VHF receiver to 121.5 MHz and actuating the unit. Tests should be limited to three audio sweeps and conducted during the first five minutes after any hour. If the testing must be done at any other time, it should be coordinated with the closest FAA Control Tower or Flight Service Station. (See Advisory Circular 20-81 for additional information.)

How can the pilot tell if the locator is on?

The signal, because of the close proximity of the locator, will probably saturate the communications receiver regardless of the frequency it is on. However, accidental triggering of the ELT should be checked during the pre-takeoff check and before engine shut down by turning the VHF receiver to 121.5 or 243.0 MHz and listening for the ELT signal.

What should be done if an ELT is activated accidentally or by an unauthorized person?

If audio sweeps are heard and it is determined that they are coming from the airplane, turn off the ELT immediately. The pilot in command of an ELT-equipped plane is responsible for accidental inflight signalling by an ELT. If the plane is parked, the owner is liable. The Communications Act of 1934 prescribes fines and imprisonment for "the willful transmission of unauthorized signals on emergency frequencies." If you experience malfunctioning of the ELT, report the incident to the FAA through the "Malfunction Defects" program to provide a factual basis for corrective action. Contact any FAA District Office for the proper forms to report the malfunction.

What should you do if you hear an ELT signal?

The FAA suggests that you notify the nearest FAA ground facility stating your position when the ELT signal was first heard and when it was last heard. You need do nothing more unless requested by the ground facility. However, if you have actually discovered the site of a crash, and circumstances permit, you have the option of advising that you will circle the crash site to guide rescue teams.

U.S. Department of Transportation
Federal Aviation Administration

VFR PILOT EXAM-O-GRAM° NO. 55

TERMINAL RADAR SERVICE AREAS (TRSAs)

"STAGE III"

Due to implementation of an increasing number of TRSAs at certain busy terminal locations, written tests for pilot certification require a knowledge of these areas and the service provided within them. This Exam-O-Gram is to help pilots in becoming familiar with the areas and the service provided.

In the interest of safety, TRSAs have been established at airports where the volume of different types — small, large, slow, and fast — of VFR and IFR aircraft can best be served by radar sequencing and separation. The service provided within a TRSA is called STAGE III SERVICE. DO NOT confuse Stage III service with Stage I or Stage II Service. Stage I Service provides traffic information and limited vectoring to VFR aircraft on a workload permitting basis. Stage II Service is to adjust the flow of arriving VFR and IFR aircraft into the traffic pattern in a safe and orderly manner and to provide radar traffic information to departing VFR aircraft. Stage III Service provides <u>separation</u> between all <u>participating</u> VFR aircraft and all IFR aircraft operating within TRSAs. Radar equipped FAA Air Traffic Control (ATC) facilities provide Stage III Service.

Arriving aircraft landing at airports within a TRSA and aircraft desiring to transit the TRSA should contact <u>Approach Control</u> or <u>Departure Control</u> (as the case may be) from outside the TRSA on the specified frequencies in relation to geographical fixes depicted on TRSA Charts. The TRSA Charts are found in the Graphic Notices and Supplemental Data publication.

Departing aircraft will be issued a clearance by the control tower advising them when to contact Departure Control and the frequency to use.

AIM—Basic Flight Information and ATC Procedures manual contains a detailed explanation of the program. A list of participating terminals, TRSA Charts, flight procedures, ATC procedures, and a further description of services provided are contained in Graphic Notices and Supplemental Data.

Stage III Services within a TRSA are provided on a voluntary pilot participation basis. Pilot participation is urged but is not mandatory. ATC takes the positive approach and assumes that all VFR aircraft want the service unless the pilot advises otherwise.

Remember, unless you advise you do not want Stage III Service when you contact Ground Control for taxi information or Approach Control for radar service, you will be issued a clearance. Be prepared to copy the clearance!

Typical Departure Communications Procedures.

PILOT: "Ground control Airwing 1567 Papa, at Ace Aviation, VFR southeastward, have information BRAVO, ready to taxi."

GROUND: "Airwing 1567 Papa, have your clearance; after takeoff turn right heading 080, maintain VFR at or below 4,500, departure frequency 121.05, squawk 0464. Taxi to Runway 35 via taxiway A."

PILOT: "1567 Papa, roger."

TOWER (after takeoff): "Airwing 1567 Papa, contact departure."

PILOT: "1567 Papa, roger."

PILOT: "Departure, Airwing 1567 Papa, turning to 080."

DEPARTURE: "Airwing 1567 Papa, radar contact, traffic 2 o'clock, 3 miles northbound, turn right heading 125°."

PILOT: "1567 Papa, looking, turning right to 125°."

DEPARTURE (later): "Airwing 67 Papa, 25 miles southeast of Columbia, fly on course, squawk VFR, radar service terminated."

PILOT: "67 Papa, roger."

Typical Arrival Communications Procedures.

PILOT: "Columbia Approach Control, Airwing 7651 Alfa, Little Mountain, heading 120°, 3,500 feet, squawking 1200, landing at Columbia METRO with information BRAVO."

APPROACH: "Airwing 7651 Alfa, squawk 0410 for identification."

PILOT: "7651 Alfa squawking 0410."

APPROACH: "Airwing 51 Alfa, radar contact, turn right heading 140° for vector to Runway 5. Maintain VFR, descend and maintain 2,500 feet."

PILOT: "51 Alfa leaving 3,500."

APPROACH (later): "Airwing 51 Alfa, traffic a Rovercraft, 12 o'clock, 3 miles eastbound. Advise when you have the Rovercraft in sight."

PILOT: "51 Alfa, I have visual contact with the Rovercraft."

APPROACH: "Airwing 51 Alfa, follow the Rovercraft, contact tower on 119.5."

PILOT: "51 Alfa, roger."

As the above arrival procedures illustrate, ATC may provide nonradar separation when prevailing conditions permit. If the pilot has visual contact with the preceding aircraft, he may be directed to follow it for a "visual approach" or to depart the TRSA, as the case may be.

This service is not to be interpreted as relieving pilots of their responsibilities to see and avoid other aircraft operating in basic VFR conditions. Assignment of radar headings and/or altitudes are based on the provision that a pilot operating in accordance with VFR is expected to advise ATC if compliance with an assigned route, radar heading, or altitude will cause the pilot to violate such rules.

FLIGHT IN THE REGION OF REVERSED COMMAND
IN RELATION TO TAKEOFFS AND LANDINGS

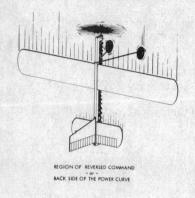

REGION OF REVERSED COMMAND
- or -
BACK SIDE OF THE POWER CURVE

The aeronautical knowledge requirements, set forth in Federal Aviation Regulations for pilot certification, place emphasis on basic aerodynamics and principles of flight. Consequently, FAA written tests contain test items relating to these subject areas.

This Exam-O-Gram deals with a rather complex and often misunderstood subject as it relates principally to propeller driven airplanes. Modern aerodynamics manuals refer to this as the "Region of Reversed Command," and devote one or more chapters to explaining its meaning. It is the intent of this Exam-O-Gram, to explain in layman's language and through the use of simple illustrations, flight in the regions of normal and reversed command, without the use of mathematical formulas, symbols, or equations. These few pages, though perhaps an oversimplification of a complicated subject, should serve as a stimulus for further study.

The following brief definitions of terms used in the text are presented to refresh the reader's memory:

PARASITE DRAG -- the drag not directly associated with lift (form and skin friction) and which predominates in the region of high-speed flight. NOTE: An increase in the parasite area of an airplane may be brought about by the deflections of flaps or extension of the landing gear.

INDUCED DRAG -- the drag caused by lift.

TOTAL DRAG -- the sum of the parasite and induced drags.

EQUILIBRIUM -- a state of balance or equality between opposing forces. An airplane is in a state of equilibrium when the sum of all forces and the sum of all moments acting on it are equal to zero.

BRAKE HORSEPOWER -- the power output of the reciprocating engine is determined by attaching a brake or load device to the output shaft. Hence, the term brake horsepower (BHP) is used to denote engine power.

POWER REQUIRED -- the aerodynamic properties of the airplane generally determine the power requirements at various conditions of flight, while the powerplant capabilities generally determine the power available at various conditions of flight. When the airplane is in steady level flight the condition of equilibrium must prevail. An unaccelerated condition of flight is achieved when lift equals weight, and the powerplant is set for a thrust equal to the airplane drag.

POWER REQUIRED CURVE -- the power required to achieve equilibrium in constant-altitude flight at various airspeeds. The power required curve illustrates the fact that at low airspeeds near the stall or minimum control speed, the power setting required for steady level flight is quite high.

○ ○ ○

WHAT DOES "FLIGHT IN THE REGION OF NORMAL COMMAND" MEAN? Flight in the region of normal command means that while holding a constant altitude, a higher airspeed requires a higher power setting and a lower airspeed requires a lower power setting. The majority of all airplane flying (climb, cruise, and maneuvers) is conducted in the region of normal command.

WHAT DOES "FLIGHT IN THE REGION OF REVERSED COMMAND" MEAN? Flight in the region of reversed command means that a higher airspeed requires a lower power setting and a lower airspeed requires a higher power setting to hold altitude. It does not imply that a decrease in power will result in higher airspeed, or that an increase in power will produce lower airspeed. The region of reversed command is encountered in the low speed phases of flight. Flight speeds below the speed for maximum endurance (lowest point on the power curve) require higher power settings with a decrease in airspeed. Since the need to increase the required power setting with decreased speed is contrary to the normal command of flight, the regime of flight speeds between the speed for minimum required power setting and the stall speed (or minimum control speed) is termed the region of reversed command. In the region of reversed command, a decrease in airspeed must be accompanied by an increased power setting in order to maintain steady flight. Simply stated — it takes a lot of power to fly at very slow airspeeds.

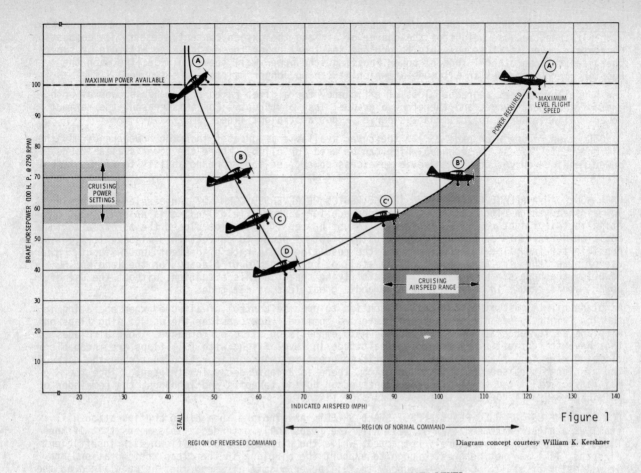

A LIGHT AIRPLANE IN A CLEAN CONFIGURATION AT SEA LEVEL

In order to chart the perrormance of a light airplane in the available space on the diagram above, it was necessary to somewhat distort the lower portion of the power required curve. This diagram illustrates that high power settings are required to fly fast or very slow. For example:

  Airplane Position A — requires full power to hold altitude at 45 MPH. At position A' the airplane is flying with full power to attain maximum level flight speed. Any attempt to increase the airspeed at position A' will result in a loss of altitude.

  Position B — requires 70 HP to maintain altitude at 55 MPH. Using the same power setting (70 HP) at position B' the airplane will maintain steady level flight while holding altitude and maintaining 104 MPH.

  Position C — 55 HP is required to maintain altitude at approximately 58 MPH. With the same power setting the airplane will attain a speed of 87 MPH at position C'. At position C', if the angle of attack is increased the airplane will climb and fly slower -or- if the angle of attack is reduced the airplane will lose altitude and fly faster than 87 MPH. NOTE: Increasing or decreasing the angle of attack at positions A' and B' would produce similar results.

  Position D — the aircraft is maintaining altitude at the lowest power (40 HP) and airspeed combination. Increasing the angle of attack at this point will not produce a climb — but a loss of altitude. Also, any reduction in the angle of attack will result in a loss of altitude.

WHAT DOES THE SPEED OF AIRPLANE D ON THE POWER REQUIRED CURVE REPRESENT? The Best Endurance Speed.— It is the lowest point on the curve. Since this is the lowest brake horsepower which will sustain level flight, it also will be the lowest fuel flow — hence, best endurance.

o o o

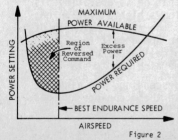

Figure 2

The illustration to the left shows the "maximum power available" as a curved line. Lower power settings such as cruise power would also appear in a similar curve. The bottom of the power required curve is more realistic in this illustration than the one shown above.
WHY IS THE POWER AVAILABLE A CURVED LINE? If the engine produces full power at the rated RPM in level flight, at other airspeeds lower than maximum the engine does not turn up its rated RPM, but gradually loses RPM, even though full throttle is being used. This can be demonstrated in a fixed-pitch propeller equipped airplane by raising the nose above cruising level flight attitude and noting a decrease in RPM. (cont'd)

-2-

<u>Power at high altitudes</u> — the power produced by the unsupercharged aircraft engine also decreases with altitude, because weight of the charge of air and the oxygen content necessary for combustion decreases. Even if it is possible to prolong sea-level power to some greater altitude by super-charging, or some other method of power boosting, the power will inevitably decline when the boosting method reaches an altitude at which it can no longer maintain a set power.

The propeller suffers a gradual loss of efficiency for a given rated engine horsepower at both ends of the speed range, and therefore a gradual loss of thrust. For this reason, the Maximum Power Available Curve is just that, a <u>curve</u> — not a straight line.

NOTE: See Figure 2 on page 2. If the power available is greater than the power required, the difference is "excess horsepower" which can be used for climb. Where the power available and power required curves cross, there is no excess power, and therefore no ability to climb at that airspeed.

o o o

WHEN WOULD AN AIRPLANE BE OPERATING IN THE REGION OF REVERSED COMMAND? An airplane performing a low airspeed, high-pitch attitude power approach for a short field landing is an example of operating in this flight regime. Imagine what might happen if the pilot closed the throttle to idle position during this approach. Then by using a lot of power to correct this mistake it might be possible for the pilot to reduce or stop the resulting rapid rate of descent, but without further use of power the airplane would probably stall or be incapable of flaring for the landing. Merely lowering the nose of the airplane to regain flying speed in this situation, without the use of power, would result in a rapid sink rate and a great loss of altitude.

Airplane pilots must give particular attention to precise control of airspeed when operating in the low flight speeds of the region of reversed command. Now consider the use of wing flaps on airplane performance at low flight speeds with emphasis on climb performance. Some airplanes that have the capability of maintaining altitude in level flight with full flaps are incapable of climbing with full flaps extended. Drag is so great in this configuration that when the nose of the airplane is raised to establish a climb, there is a rapid decay in airspeed. Since the majority of pilot caused airplane accidents occur during takeoffs and landings, the remainder of this Exam-O-Gram is devoted to these phases of flight.

HOW DOES THE USE OF FULL FLAPS AFFECT STALL SPEED? An airplane in a clean configuration will stall at a higher airspeed than it will with the flaps fully extended. This means that if the flaps are rapidly or prematurely retracted, while the airplane is being flown with insufficient airspeed, lift may not be great enough to support the airplane in the clean configuration, and it will sink or stall. On a go-around with full power a safe airspeed must be maintained as the flaps are slowly retracted — in small increments.

SHOULD WING FLAPS BE USED FOR TAKEOFF? Certain Airplane Owner's Manuals do recommend the use of partial wing flaps (10°-20°) to reduce the ground run on short or soft field takeoffs. The use of full flaps on takeoff, however, is not recommended because of the great amount of drag they produce. A go-around with full flaps extended is a situation similar to the full flap takeoff.

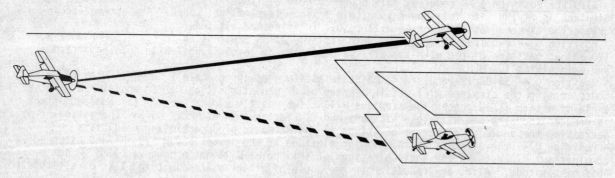

A GO-AROUND WITH FULL FLAPS

Figure 3

In the illustration above, suppose the pilot of the airplane on the landing approach applies full throttle for a go-around because another airplane is on the runway, but due to a burned-out flap motor fuse, is unable to retract the fully extended flaps. Assume also that he is operating his airplane at near maximum certificated gross weight, or at an airport having a high elevation or high density altitude. Any one or a combination of these situations plus the tremendous drag of the flaps will require considerable pilot skill if the airplane is to gain enough altitude to circle the airport and land. Any misuse of the controls, such as overcontrolling or banking too steeply while operating in the "Region of Reversed Command," may cause the airplane to stall.

With a margin of only a few MPH between climbing, holding altitude, and descending, the airplane may cease its slow rate of climb and start descending or even stall, while the occupants are distracted in their attempt to identify or correct the cause of the malfunction. (cont'd)

Actual failure of the electric flap motor would require operating in this high drag configuration until the airplane lands. ○ ○ ○

Most Airplane Owner's Manuals of present-day trainers state that full flaps are not recommended at any time for takeoff. In recent years an average of ten serious accidents have occurred each year as a result of pilots attempting to take off with full flaps extended.

Accident Report Summaries all recite much the same story as the excerpts which follow: "A solo student performing touch-and-go landings in an airplane attempted a takeoff with full flaps. He lost control of the airplane, closed the throttle, and the airplane flipped over on its back. He stated that his instructor had never demonstrated how the aircraft would react or respond when full flaps were used for takeoff. A low time student in a new and strange situation set the stage for this accident."

"A 200 hour private pilot with a passenger attempted to take off with full flaps. The airplane climbed to 150 feet, stalled and rotated one-half turn to the left and struck the ground nosedown in a near vertical attitude at impact."

"A commercial pilot with a passenger attempted to take off with full flaps. The airplane, which was 15 pounds over gross weight, staggered into the air to a height of about 30 feet. Power was reduced and the airplane descended at a steep angle with no flare for touchdown. The nosewheel collapsed on impact."

○ ○ ○

<u>The slow rate of climb or inability to climb to traffic pattern altitude with full flaps presents the greatest problem!</u> Good pilot technique is necessary to obtain a slow rate of climb under ideal conditions. Climb performance is even more critical at high altitudes, higher weights, or high temperatures.

○ ○ ○ ○ ○

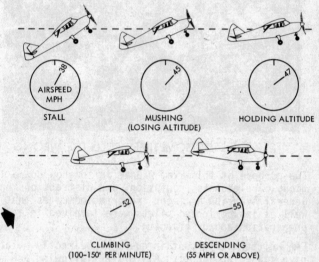

NOTE: Indicated airspeeds may be unreliable near the stall or in steep pitch attitudes. The airplanes and indicated airspeeds shown in this illustration are fictitious.

ATTEMPTING TO CLIMB (FULL THROTTLE) WITH FULL FLAPS EXTENDED

Operation in the region of reversed command does not imply that great control difficulty and dangerous conditions exist. For many aircraft, normal approach speeds are well within the region of reversed command. However, flight in the region of reversed command does amplify any errors of basic flying technique. Hence, proper flying technique and precise control of airplane are most necessary in the region of reversed command.

-4-

PILOT INDUCED ACCIDENTS

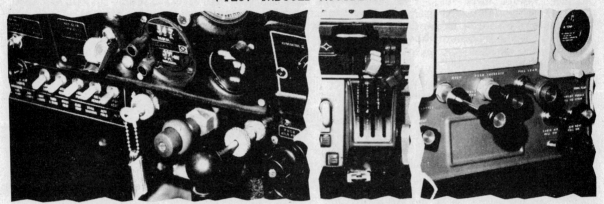

PILOTS SOMETIMES PULL THE WRONG HANDLE OR FLIP THE WRONG SWITCH

The purpose of this Exam-O-Gram is to show how a lack of knowledge, inadequate preflight preparation, carelessness, confusion, and distractions have contributed to accidents. A study of many
General Aviation Accident reports indicates that an alarming number of experienced pilots, as
well as inexperienced pilots were involved in accidents that resulted from "inadequate preflight
preparation and/or planning."

FAA written tests contain questions directly related to many of the conditions and factors that
have caused accidents. All of the following are subject matter areas of aeronautical knowledge
covered in written tests:
   Preflight planning; use of the carburetor heat/mixture/throttle/propeller controls; pilot
   privileges/limitations; aircraft cruise performance charts; aircraft loading; fuel consumption; the effect of strong headwinds on aircraft range; etc.

Lack of knowledge in these subjects, combined with inadequate preflight preparation and careless
flying habits, virtually assures that pilot error will be a significant factor in a high percentage of aircraft accidents. Also, some persons become involved in accidents by attempting to fly
an airplane when: (1) there are pressing problems unrelated to flying on their minds; (2) they
are not sufficiently alert; (3) their proficiency is marginal; or (4) they are not thoroughly familiar with or "at home" in the airplane being flown.

Experienced pilots as well as student pilots can benefit from the review of accident reports. We
should all learn from the mistakes of others, yet it seems many persons must make the same costly
mistakes themselves before they really learn. Reading the case reports which follow should make
it clear that accidents are often related to a lack of knowledge, in addition to one or more of
the factors mentioned above.

IMPROPER USE OF POWERPLANT CONTROLS

HOW HAS A LACK OF KNOWLEDGE OF USING THE MIXTURE CONTROL APPARENTLY CONTRIBUTED TO AIRCRAFT
ACCIDENTS? Although pilots are familiar with stopping the engine after a flight by placing the
mixture control in idle cutoff, some persons apparently are not familiar with how an engine re-
sponds in flight as this control is being moved toward the idle cutoff position. This is true
when operating with high-power settings, and also during glides with the throttle closed as the
propeller continues to windmill with the mixture in idle cutoff.

Reports for a 3-year period showed that an average of 16 accidents occurred each year as a result
of pilots unintentionally pulling a wrong handle--the mixture control instead of the intended
control. There were 38 "mismanagement of mixture control" accidents reported for a period of
2 1/2 years for just one popular make airplane. These pilot-induced emergencies were caused by
pilots unintentionally creating complete power failures through improper use of the mixture
control. Accident reports recite much the same story as the excerpts which follow:

★ "A student pilot on a solo cross-country flight was cruising at 6,500 feet, and being unfamiliar with the mixture control, made no attempt to lean out the mixture. When the
   engine started to run rough the student assumed the problem to be carburetor ice. After
   applying what he thought was carburetor heat--the engine sputtered and quit. After an
   emergency landing was made, the accident investigating team found the mixture control in
   the full lean (idle cutoff) position."

★ "When the aircraft was removed from the river, the mixture control was in the "idle cutoff" position. The pilot stated that he closed the throttle and thought he applied full carburetor heat. When the engine seemed to be idling too slowly the throttle was advanced but the engine did not respond. The pilot assumed a fuel tank was empty and hurriedly switched tanks, and since this didn't solve the problem, an emergency landing was attempted on the river bank."

★ "A business executive accompanied by two passengers departed on a business trip in a single-engine airplane. Soon after takeoff the pilot experienced complete power failure, and the airplane was landed straight ahead outside the airport. Investigation revealed the mixture control positioned three-fourths of the way to full lean. The pilot stated that he was monitoring the tachometer and manifold pressure gauge and didn't notice which control he used to change the prop pitch."

Pilots should <u>visually</u> check a control prior to operating it, but this is not always practiced. During takeoffs and landings many pilots manipulate controls by touch while monitoring other traffic, communicating with the tower, or scanning instruments. When a pilot is not mindful of which knob, lever, switch, or handle his hands are touching, the stage is set for a pilot-induced emergency. This is especially true when the pilot's attention is diverted by some unusual circumstance or outside distraction.

o o o

HOW HAVE FLIGHT INSTRUCTORS BEEN INVOLVED IN MISUSE OF THE MIXTURE CONTROL ACCIDENTS?

There were seven accidents of this type involving one popular make single-engine trainer, in a 1 1/2 year period. The following are "Brief Descriptions" of several of the accidents:

★ 1. "Instructor pulled mixture control for simulated emergency and engine would not restart."

★ 2. "Flight instructor moved mixture control to idle cutoff position to simulate engine failure. Could not get engine restarted. Battery was dead and alternator was inoperative."

★ 3. "Flight instructor pulled mixture control to idle cutoff to simulate engine failure at 800 feet. Engine did not respond when control was placed in RICH."

There were five similar accidents involving flight instructors in 1975. Two of these concerned light twin-engine aircraft - one on final approach and the other on takeoff at 20 feet AGL.

NOTE: The FAA inspector training policy for simulating partial or complete power malfunctions in single-engine aircraft is by smooth use of the throttle ONLY. The objective of simulated power malfunctions is not to shock the students but to train them in proper procedures and control of the aircraft.

WHAT MAY HAPPEN WHEN PILOTS ATTEMPT TO FLY AIRPLANES WITH WHICH THEY ARE NOT FAMILIAR?

Select One - Carefully.

★ "Shortly after lift-off the student pilot experienced a reduction in power and pulled <u>a handle to apply carburetor heat</u>. The airplane continued to lose power and was landed outside the airport boundary.

The Student Pilot Certificate had been endorsed for operating a similar earlier model (carburetor equipped) airplane of the same make that was being flown. The student had never flown an airplane equipped with fuel injection, a fuel boost pump, or a controllable pitch propeller, though the airplane involved in the accident was so equipped. Investigation revealed that the fuel boost pump was in the LOW operating position whereas the checklist specified that it be turned OFF during takeoff. The <u>cabin heat control</u> was in the full ON position and the student guessed that was the handle he pulled!"

WHAT ARE SOME OF THE MORE COMMON PILOT-INDUCED ACCIDENTS THAT HAVE RESULTED FROM USING THE WRONG HANDLE OR SWITCH?

Retracting the gear instead of the flaps after landing; retracting the gear while attempting to lock the parking brakes; turning off the ignition toggle switches while attempting to turn on the landing lights; etc.

o o o

WHAT ARE THE HAZARDS OF NOT COMPLETING CERTAIN COCKPIT DUTIES?

Pilots who start one flight operation or procedure, and proceed to another operation before completing the first, may become involved in an accident simply because the first task was never completed. The following examples are typical:

Example 1.- A pilot of a multiengine airplane decides to check the operation of the crossfeed while taxiing from the ramp prior to takeoff. After placing the selector in the crossfeed position the pilot is distracted by a question from a passenger, another aircraft taxiing close by, or radio communications. The pilot intended to switch the fuel selectors back to the main fuel tanks after determining that the crossfeed was operating properly, but failed to do so because of the distractions.

Example 2.- Airplane "A" is on the downwind leg of the traffic pattern when airplane "B" squeezes in the pattern ahead of "A." The pilot of airplane "A" had started to perform the pre-landing cockpit check when this distraction occurred. In a situation like this, unfortunately, some persons react with anger which sets the stage for a gear-up landing or a more serious accident.

INADEQUATE PREFLIGHT?

★ ATP Pilot -- Ran off the runway.
 Remarks -- Movement of copilot's right rudder pedal obstructed by a whiskey bottle.

★ Private Pilot -- Collided with parked aircraft.
 Remarks -- Did not remove right wing tiedown, started to taxi, tried to cut mixture control, but opened throttle.

HOW MIGHT AN INCOMPLETE PRETAKEOFF CHECK RESULT IN FUEL STARVATION?

Here is the way it happened to one pilot.

★ "An experienced private pilot flying his own airplane departed an airport with full fuel tanks. After a stopover of several hours at a nearby airport, the pilot hurriedly taxied to a runway for takeoff.

Airplane lost power at an altitude of approximately 50 feet on takeoff and settled back to surface. With only 437 feet of runway remaining, pilot was unable to stop, but chain link fence at field boundary turned the trick. Pilot was unable to recall position of fuel selector before takeoff, but noted that it was in OFF position after the accident. He stated that he had <u>never</u> turned fuel to the OFF position at the end of a flight."

This is an example of why a pilot should carefully check an airplane before each flight and not assume that it will remain just the same as it was on a previous flight. Many airports have people hanging around who enjoy climbing in airplanes, moving the controls, and flipping switches.

WHY DO MANY "FUEL STARVATION" ACCIDENTS OCCUR EVEN THOUGH THERE IS AMPLE FUEL ABOARD?

A common cause of engine failure is mismanagement of the fuel system. This happens frequently when the engine is fed fuel from one tank at a time.

Each year an alarming number of accidents result from pilots running a fuel tank dry. In their haste and anxiety to make an emergency landing, pilots are often back on the ground before realizing no attempt was made to switch to a tank containing fuel. In a recent year there were 59 accidents of this type.

The following accident excerpt illustrates the hazards of performing certain maneuvers while operating on one tank that contains a low level quantity of fuel.

★ "On a spiral descent from 7,500 feet engine quit and airplane landed in a field and hit a fence. Pilot had started flight with fuel only in left wing tank. The spiral down with left wing low caused the little remaining fuel to move away from tank opening to fuel line, which resulted in engine stoppage."

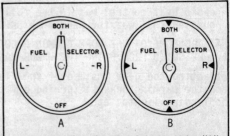

Being Familiar with Fuel Selector Valve "A" Could Lead to Trouble When Operating an Airplane Equipped with One Like "B"

FUEL STARVATION (Continued)

The pilot in command must always be alert and aware of the actions of other occupants of the airplane, as this fuel starvation accident reveals:

★ "The engine quit during climb out after takeoff and the pilot discovered the fuel had been turned off. His wife decided there was too much air blowing on her feet and used the fuel selector handle to turn off the cabin air vents. It worked! In less than a minute there was no air blowing on her feet."

o o o

DOES FUEL EXHAUSTION HAVE THE SAME MEANING AS FUEL STARVATION?

No; fuel exhaustion means all the usable fuel aboard the aircraft has been consumed. Accidents such as these are of great concern in General Aviation, because they usually result from inadequate preflight preparation or planning and pilots not being familiar with the operating limitations of their equipment. There were 75 accidents attributed to fuel exhaustion in 1975. In recent years, some pilots operating in mountainous areas of western states have encountered fuel exhaustion before reaching their destination. Fuel exhaustion accidents resulted after they had been flying with 40-50 knot headwinds or had drifted off course in strong crosswinds. Some were operating at high altitudes without leaning the mixture, while others failed to refer to the Aircraft Cruise Performance charts and other data. For this reason, FAA written tests contain test items related to these subject areas.

BRIEF DESCRIPTION OF A TYPICAL FUEL EXHAUSTION ACCIDENT

★ "Engine quit because of fuel exhaustion 3 miles short of destination with forced landing in unsuitable terrain. Contributing factors were: (1) Improper flight planning, (2) relying on fuel gauges rather than manufacturer's fuel consumption figures, (3) overflying several suitable airports where additional fuel could have been obtained, (4) adverse weather conditions and strong headwinds."

IS THE PRACTICE OF RUNNING A FUEL TANK DRY BEFORE SWITCHING TANKS CONSIDERED A SAFE PROCEDURE?

No; some aircraft engine manufacturers recommend never running a fuel tank dry as a routine procedure. When the fuel selector remains on an empty tank which has run dry, the engine-driven fuel pump draws air into the fuel system and causes vapor lock. This is also true when an electric fuel boost pump is operated with the fuel selector on an empty tank. Fuel injection equipped engines, in particular, are vulnerable to vapor lock when the fuel selector is positioned on an empty tank.

BE ALERT, KNOW YOUR LIMITATIONS AND THE LIMITATIONS OF YOUR
EQUIPMENT. LEARN FROM THE MISTAKES OF OTHERS AND AVOID
SIMILAR ACCIDENTS.

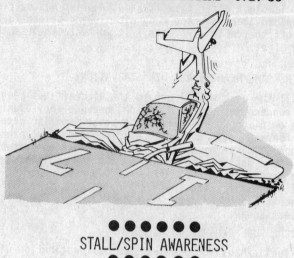

• • • • • •
STALL/SPIN AWARENESS
• • • • • •

According to a recent FAA General Aviation Stall Awareness study, stall/spin accidents occur in general aviation aircraft at an average rate of one a day. This Exam-O-Gram has been developed in an effort to make pilots more aware of the problem.

☆ ☆ ☆ ☆ ☆ ☆ ☆ ☆

WHICH PILOT LEVEL IS MOST INVOLVED IN THESE ACCIDENTS? The pilots involved in 991 of the stall/spin accidents, according to certificate, included 166 student pilots, 425 private pilots, 203 commercial pilots, 163 commercial flight instructor pilots, and 34 others. 956 of the accidents occurred during VFR weather conditions, 29 during IFR conditions, 5 in unknown conditions, and 1 in conditions below minimums. 892 of the accidents occurred during daylight, 54 at night, 40 at dusk, 4 at dawn, and 1 in unreported lighting conditions.

DURING WHAT TYPE OF OPERATION DO MOST STALL/SPIN ACCIDENTS OCCUR? 60.5 percent of all the stall/spin accidents were associated with non-commercial flying, primarily related to practice, pleasure, and business flights. 19 percent were associated with instructional dual, solo, and training flights. 14 percent were associated with commercial flying, principally in connection with aerial application or crop-control, and the remaining 6.5 percent involved miscellaneous flights.

WHAT ARE THE FACTORS INVOLVED IN PRODUCING THESE ACCIDENTS? A review of selected accidents, which are related directly or indirectly to the unintentional stall/spin occurrence include the following factors: unwarranted low flying--fuel exhaustion due to inadequate preflight preparation and/or planning--fuel starvation due to improper fuel management--alcoholic impairment of efficiency and judgment--poorly planned approach--lack of familiarity with aircraft--attempts to fly VFR into IFR weather conditions--diverted attention from operation of aircraft--water in fuel--premature lift-off--improperly loaded aircraft-weight and/or c.g.--improper soft- or short-field takeoff or landing technique--attempting takeoff from unimproved or inadequate fields--attempting takeoff or go-around with wing flaps improperly extended--improper landing go-around technique--improper crosswind takeoff or landing technique--poor judgment and/or technique in simulated forced landings--general lack of proficiency in takeoff or landing during windy, turbulent conditions.

DURING WHAT PHASE OF OPERATION DID THESE ACCIDENTS OCCUR? 238 or 24 percent of the stall/spin accidents occurred during the takeoff phase of flight. All but one of these occurred during the initial climb. 295 or 40 percent occurred during the in-flight phase. Only 70 of these or 7 percent of the study group could be accounted for in the specific phases described as "climb to cruise," "normal cruise," and "descending." The other 325 in-flight accidents, except for four cases, were associated with "acrobatics," "buzzing," "low passes," agricultural and various other operations. The remaining 358 stall/spin accidents (36 percent of the study group) occurred during the landing phase of flight. Most, however, related specifically to "traffic pattern-circling," "final approach," and "go-around." Fatal stall/spins numbered 73 in the takeoff phase, 107 in the landing phase, and 235 in the in-flight phase. The ratio of fatal stall/spin occurrences to the total number (about 30 percent) within a given phase of flight was approximately the same in both takeoff and landing. In the in-flight phase, however, this ratio (about 60 percent) was twice as great.

RECOVERY FROM A STALLED CONDITION IS QUITE SIMPLE IN CONVENTIONAL AIRCRAFT IF SUFFICIENT ALTITUDE IS AVAILABLE. To recover from a stall, the angle of attack must be decreased and, in many cases, the airspeed increased. The airspeed at which the stall occurs is the stalling speed and is defined for level, unaccelerated flight as the "minimum speed at which the airplane can develop a lift equal to the weight of the airplane." The altitude required for recovery varies from one airplane to another but for the power-off configuration, several hundred feet is typical of most light single-engine airplanes.

AT WHAT AIRSPEED WILL A STALL OCCUR? A stall may occur at any airspeed, depending on the load factor or "g" force that is generated. The stall is a function only of the critical angle of attack of the wing. A stall that occurs at speeds higher than the minimum speed as defined above is called an accelerated stall. Accelerated stalls often occur during aerobatics, buzzing, aerial application, etc., where the associated maneuvers are characterized by steep pullups or steep turns. The classification of an accident as a stall type of accident is based on statements from the pilot and/or the observations of eyewitnesses, the attitude of the airplane, the conditions and circumstances of flight prior to impact, and an evaluation of the ground and wreckage evidence.

WHAT CAUSES A SPIN TO DEVELOP? A spin, because of the abrupt entry, rapid rate of rotation, and general disorienting effect, is considerably more violent than a stall. A spin results when a sufficient degree of rolling or yawing control input is imposed on an airplane in the stalled condition. WITHOUT A STALL, A SPIN CANNOT OCCUR. Thus, an accidental spin might result from stalling an aircraft due to "failure to obtain/maintain flying speed" in conjunction with "improper operation of the flight controls." With the controls fixed in the pro-spin direction, spin rotation, once initiated, is generally self-sustaining. The control inputs and the altitude required for recovery are much more critical for spins than for stalls. Spins at relatively low altitudes, even incipient spins where the rotation has not fully developed, are generally catastrophic. The substantiation of an incipient spin, however, is often difficult or impossible since the spin motion prior to impact may not be developed sufficiently to enable an eyewitness to observe the rotation or to result in conspicuous ground/wreckage patterns.

HOW CAN UNINTENTIONAL SPINS BE AVOIDED? A spin cannot occur until an aircraft has stalled, therefore proper stall avoidance training also provides spin avoidance.

WHAT IS THE KEY TO HELP A PILOT AVOID FALLING VICTIM TO THE DISTRACTIONS THAT LEAD TO STALL/ SPIN TYPE ACCIDENTS?

A KEY
TO
AVIATION
SAFETY

KNOWLEDGE

BY EMPHASIZING TRAINING TO

AVOID THE UNINTENTIONAL STALL.

The justification for this approach is that previous training may have emphasized the performance of an intentional stall. The accident problem, however, is created by unintentional stalls caused by distraction of the pilot from the primary job of flying the airplane. The question is, how can a pilot be prevented from becoming a victim to these distractions. The flight instructor can, by simulating critical attitudes and altitudes and creating distracting situations, educate the pilot in unintentional stall/spin avoidance. One example of such a distraction could be that of asking the pilot to retrieve a pencil or chart during flight at minimum controllable airspeed.

WHAT OTHER CLASSIFICATION OF ACCIDENTS MAY HAVE AS ITS BASIC CAUSE, AN INADVERTENT STALL? Some have been listed as: "Undershoot;" or "Hard Landing," "Premature Lift-off," or "Improper Level-off."

WHY WERE THESE ACCIDENTS NOT CLASSIFIED AS STALL/SPIN ACCIDENTS? Because they occur at such low altitudes, there is not time nor space for them to develop to the spin stage.

HOW CAN PREMATURE LIFT-OFF RESULT IN A STALL? When an airplane is flown off the surface below the recommended takeoff safety speed, the wing is near the stall angle of attack. Unless power is available to accelerate to a higher airspeed, or altitude is available to lower the angle of attack, the slightest error in control usage could result in a stall.

HOW DOES "IMPROPER LEVEL-OFF," "HARD LANDING," OR "UNDERSHOOT" RESULT FROM STALL? By using considerable back-pressure and nose-up trim to maintain approach speed. The aircraft is sinking in a manner which produces a very high angle of attack with reference to the relative wind. The aircraft is very near the stall angle, while the attitude in relation to the horizon causes the pilot to feel otherwise.

HOW CAN A HEAVILY LOADED AIRPLANE CONTRIBUTE TO A STALL? When flying a heavily loaded airplane at slow speeds, a high angle of attack is required to maintain flight at a constant altitude. It may therefore, require only a little turbulence or mishandling of the airplane to increase the angle of attack and result in the airplane stalling.

DURING TURNS HOW ARE STALLS CAUSED BY AN INCREASE IN LOAD FACTOR?

Bank angle in degrees	Load factor	Percent increase in stall speed	Percent increase in induced drag (at constant velocity)
0	1.0000	0	0
5	1.0038	0.2	0.8
10	1.0154	0.7	3.1
15	1.0353	1.7	7.2
20	1.0642	3.2	13.3
25	1.1034	5.0	21.7
30	1.1547	7.5	33.3
35	1.2208	10.5	49.0
40	1.3054	14.3	70.4
45	1.4142	18.9	100.0
60	2.000	41.4	300.0

In a turn made at a constant altitude, we have to furnish the lift NORMALLY required to sustain the aircraft in level flight, plus the ADDITIONAL lift necessary to overcome the centrifugal force developed in the turn. We do this by adding back pressure on the controls. This increases the angle of attack of the wing with reference to the Relative Wind. It can be seen that in a level turn with a 60° bank, a load factor of 2.0 is produced. This means the angle of attack must be increased to where the wing is supporting twice the normal weight of the aircraft. This is impossible for the average aircraft because of the related increase in stall speed and increase in DRAG. In fact, very few light aircraft at maximum gross weight, have sufficient power to maintain more than 45° to 50° banked turns.

HOW CAN A PILOT BE CARELESS ENOUGH TO STALL AN AIRPLANE DURING A TURN? Stalls are relatively easy in some of our modern airplanes which have light aileron pressures. Therefore, in these airplanes a pilot may inadvertently steepen the bank to where the back pressure required increases the angle of attack of the wing to the Stall point. It should be remembered that many times Stall accidents occur from a combination of slow-flight and angle of bank during a turn. The results are cumulative. If the airplane is flown too slow requiring large deflections of the control surfaces, the increased DRAG will result in airplane performance deteriorating even further. This might readily happen during a take-off or landing at a slow airspeed.

ATTITUDES ARE LIKE ALTITUDES, WATCH THEM OR YOU'LL WIND UP ON THE GROUND

WEIGHT AND BALANCE

In one recent year, improper weight and balance was a factor in 39 airplane accidents, 12 of which caused fatalities. Most of the accidents occurred during the takeoff, climb, or landing phase with the airplane either over gross weight or the center of gravity out of the approved limits. This type of accident could have been avoided.

Weight and balance limits are established for each airplane for two principal reasons; the effect on the airplane's structure and the effect on flight characteristics. All aircraft are flight tested at maximum gross weight and within the center of gravity range at which the aircraft is designed. If these limits are exceeded during flight, control of the airplane may be difficult, if not impossible. Exam-O-Gram No. 13 also discusses the effects of improper weight and balance.

WHAT EFFECT DOES EXCESSIVE WEIGHT HAVE ON AIRCRAFT PERFORMANCE? Excessive weight reduces the airplane's performance in almost every respect. Some of the most important effects are:

* higher takeoff speed	* lower maximum altitude	* shorter range
* longer takeoff run	* higher stalling speed	* higher landing speed
* reduced maneuverability	* reduced cruising speed	* longer landing roll

WHAT EFFECT DOES EXCESSIVE WEIGHT HAVE ON AIRCRAFT STRUCTURES? Aircraft are designed to withstand certain load factors. If the aircraft is over gross weight it could exceed its design load factor (G-load), resulting in structural damage. In normal unaccellerated flight the aircraft's load factor is 1 G, which means the wings are supporting the aircraft's total weight only. Turns, maneuvers, stall and spin recoveries, and turbulent air can impose an additional load factor. For instance, in an abrupt pullup from a dive, a load factor of 4-5 G's might be experienced. This would mean the wings are supporting the equivalent of 4-5 times the actual weight of the airplane, and if the airplane's limit load factor is 3.0, it would be exceeded by 1-2 G's. If the air was turbulent during the pullup, an even greater load (e.g. 9 G's) could be imposed because a sudden vertical gust would suddenly increase the wings' angle of attack even more. This could cause severe damage to the airplane.

✳ ✳ ✳ ✳

REMEMBER IF GROSS WEIGHT IS EXCEEDED YOU MAY NEVER GET OFF THE GROUND.

✳ ✳ ✳ ✳

The aircraft's center of gravity (CG) is the point at which the airplane would balance if suspended from that point. The airplane is designed to be controllable within the CG's forward and aft limits. If the airplane were to be loaded beyond those limits it could be difficult to control.

WHAT RESULTS IF THE CG IS LOCATED FORWARD OF THE FORWARD LIMIT? For safe operation of an airplane, the pilot must have adequate control to establish the takeoff attitude and maintain a climb, and more importantly, to round-out and establish the landing attitude at specified landing speeds. A CG located forward of the forward limit might make this so difficult, the pilot would be unable to prevent the airplane from striking the ground.

WHAT RESULTS IF THE CG IS LOCATED BEHIND THE AFT LIMIT? This could result in an unstable aircraft. The further aft the CG moves the less stable the aircraft becomes, and its ability to right itself after maneuvering or being disturbed by turbulent air decreases. This is the most DANGEROUS OF LOADING CONDITIONS because of the unstable condition that may exist and the difficulty the pilot could have in controlling the airplane.

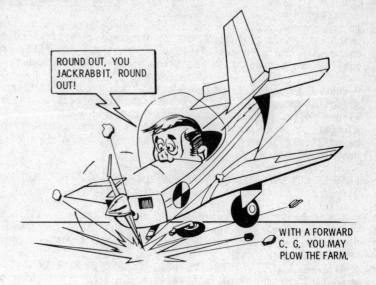

ROUND OUT, YOU JACKRABBIT, ROUND OUT!

WITH A FORWARD C. G. YOU MAY PLOW THE FARM.

With an aft CG you may not recover from a Stall or Spin

WHAT INFORMATION IS NEEDED PRIOR TO FLIGHT? Regulations require that weight and balance data be available in the aircraft before it can be operated in flight. Weight and balance records, pilot's operating manuals, equipment list, and aircraft log books contain weight and balance information. The weight and balance record shows any change in the aircraft's weight and center of gravity which resulted from changes in structures or equipment. This record should be referred to in order to determine the current empty weight and center of gravity. The equipment list shows the weight and location of the equipment installed. The pilot's operating manual has procedures for weighing the aircraft, charts or graphs to determine if the airplane's weight and balance is within limits, and often includes the equipment list. The aircraft log books show a history of maintenance performed and reflects any repair, alteration, or change which would cause a change in weight and balance.

To be sure an airplane is loaded within allowable limits, the pilot must be able to work weight and balance calculations. To do this the pilot must first be familiar with basic terminology.

Empty Weight - consists of the airframe, engines, all operating equipment which has a fixed location and is permanently installed. Includes hydraulic fluid, unusable fuel and undrainable oil, and in some airplanes includes all the oil.

Useful Load - weight of pilot, passengers, baggage, usable fuel, and drainable oil.

Maximum Gross Weight - maximum allowable weight to which the aircraft may be loaded. The aircraft empty weight plus the useful load equals the loaded gross weight.

Datum - an imaginary vertical plane or line from which all measurements of arm are taken. The datum is established by the manufacturer.

Arm - horizontal distance in inches from the reference datum line to the center of gravity of the item.

Center of Gravity (C.G.) - the point about which an aircraft would balance if it were suspended at that point.

Moment - the product of the weight of an item multiplied by its arm. Moments are expressed in pound-inches. Total moment is the weight of the aircraft multiplied by the distance between the datum and the C.G.

Station - a location in the aircraft which is identified by a number designating its distance in inches from the datum. The datum is, therefore, identified as zero.

Given the following information, work a typical weight and balance problem to determine the loaded weight and C.G. of an airplane.

Maximum gross weight	3,400 lbs.
Center of gravity range	78-86 inches
Pilot and passenger front seats	340 lbs.
2 passengers rear seats	350 lbs.
full fuel	75 gals.
*full oil (not included in empty weight)	8 qts.
baggage area 1	80 lbs.
baggage area 2	-0-

*New airplanes include full oil in the empty weight. Refer to the weight and balance date for the particular airplane you are operating to determine if oil is included in empty weight.

	WEIGHT	ARM	MOMENT/100
Airplane empty weight	2,110	78.3	1,652.1
Front seats	-----	85	-------
Rear seats	-----	121	-------
Fuel (75 gals. usable)	-----	75	-------
Oil (8 qt. capacity)	-----	25	-------
Baggage area 1	-----	150	-------
Baggage area 2	-----	195	-------

TOTALS

Step 1 - list on the weight and balance form the weight of all occupants, fuel, oil, and baggage to be carried - (remember aviation fuel weighs 6 lbs. per gallon and oil weighs 7.5 lbs. per gallon).

Step 2 - enter the moment for each item listed above (weight x arm = moment) (to simplify calculations moments are divided by 100).

Step 3 - add the weights (3,345 lbs.).

Step 4 - add the moments (2825.8 lb/in.).

Step 5 - determine the C.G. $\frac{\text{moments}/100}{\text{weight}}$ = C.G.) $(\frac{2825.8/100}{3,345}$ = 84.5).

The total loaded weight is 3,345 lbs. and the C.G. is located 84.5 inches aft of the datum; therefore, the airplane is loaded within allowable limits of 78-86 inches.

3

WHAT WOULD THE WEIGHT AND C.G. OF THE ABOVE AIRPLANE BE AFTER 40 GALLONS OF FUEL WERE BURNED? This could be done by changing the information in steps 1 and 2 to show 35 gallons of fuel (75 - 40 = 35) and then completing steps 3 and 5. The new weight would be 3,105 lbs. and the C.G. 85.2 inches.

The airplane is still within limits. The weight decreased and the C.G. moved aft.

□□□□□□□□□□□□□□

HOW WOULD THE C.G. BE AFFECTED IF 40 LBS. OF BAGGAGE IN AREA 1 WERE MOVED TO AREA 2 WITH THE AIRPLANE OTHERWISE LOADED AS IN PROBLEM 1?

Baggage moment station area 1 - 150 in.
Baggage moment station area 2 - 195 in.

Step 1 - determine the moment for areas 1 and 2. $40 \times 150 = 6,000$ $40 \times 195 = 7,800$

Step 2 - determine the moment change: $7,800 - 6,000 = \dfrac{1,800}{100} = 18$

Step 3 - add the moment change to the total moments. (If the weight were moved forward the change would be subtracted.)

Step 4 - divide the total moments by the weight: $\dfrac{2843.8/100}{3,345} = 85.3$ in. C.G.

This is within limits and the C.G. moved aft.

□□□□□□□□□□□□□□

HOW MUCH MORE WEIGHT COULD BE ADDED TO BAGGAGE AREA 2 (STATION 195) WITHOUT EXCEEDING THE AFT C.G. LIMIT?

Aircraft weight   3,345 lbs.
C.G.   Station 85.3
Aft C.G. limit   Station 86

Formula: $\dfrac{\text{added weight}}{\text{old total weight}} = \dfrac{\text{C.G. movement}}{\text{Distance between weight and new C.G.}}$

$\dfrac{\text{added weight}}{3,345} = \dfrac{.7}{109} \quad \dfrac{(86-85.3)}{195-86}$

$\dfrac{2341.5}{109} = 21.5$ lbs.

Manufacturers use many types of charts, graphs, tables, and other illustrations which simplify weight and balance calculations. A pilot should always refer to the manufacturers instructions to use these and should observe any restrictions which are placed on weight location. The different charts, graphs, tables, and illustrations will be explained in a later Exam-O-Gram.

REMEMBER A PROPERLY LOADED AIRPLANE IS A STABLE, CONTROLLABLE, SAFE AIRPLANE.

● ● ● ●

POPULAR BOOKS FOR PILOTS

by

Aviation Book Company

Available from book dealers, flight schools, or by mail directly from the Aviation Book Company. (Listed prices are subject to change without notice).

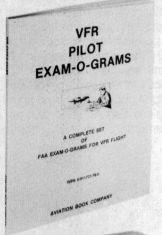

VFR PILOT EXAM-O-GRAMS
by
Aviation Book Co.

Reprinted in this book are all current Exam-o-grams pertaining to VFR flight that have been issued by the FAA. These are brief and timely illustrated explanations of important aeronautical knowledge items, including concepts and procedures that are critical to aviation safety, common misconceptions among new pilots, and areas which cause general difficulty in FAA written tests. 128 pages. 183 photos and drawings. Paperbound.

IFR PILOT EXAM-O-GRAMS
by
Aviation Book Co.

In this book are all current FAA Exam-o-grams pertaining to instrument flight. These are timely, illustrated explanations of important aeronautical knowledge items, including concepts and procedures that are critical to aviation safety, common misconceptions, and areas which cause general difficulty in FAA instrument written tests. 96 pages. 98 drawings. Paperbound.

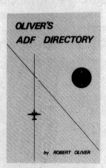

OLIVER'S ADF DIRECTORY
by
Robert Oliver

Directory of airports in the conterminous United States, Alaska, Mexico, and the Caribbean area, and their distances and bearings from commercial radio stations, LOM's, NDB's, and RBn's. Also provided are type of facility, station identification letters, frequencies, power, and hours of operation. Airports are listed alphabetically for each state. 96-page, paperbound book.

AIRMAN'S INFORMATION MANUAL
by
Aviation Book Company

Walter P. Winner, Editor. To acquaint student pilots with basic flight and operational procedures as recommended or required by the Federal Aviation Administration, and to serve as a "refresher" for all licensed pilots. Published since 1966, regular revised editions have been leading ground school texts and reference manuals to provide pilots with this vital knowledge. The FAA periodical entitled "Airman's Information Manual" includes basic flight information and air traffic control procedures that every pilot (student or experienced) must understand, so the most recent issue of it is reprinted in its entirety in this popular text, including the Pilot/Controller Glossary of aviation definitions. Other government periodicals that contain important flight data for pilots are the "Airport Facility Directory" and the "Notices to Airmen". So that student pilots can become familiar with the contents of these helpful publications, and learn how to use the data, pertinent excerpts of each are also included. 304 pp. Well-illustrated. Includes latest supplements. Heavy paper covers.

FEDERAL AVIATION REGULATIONS FOR PILOTS
by
Aviation Book Company

Popular text and reference manual that contains the latest *complete reprints* of current FARs that all pilots must know and abide by while piloting aircraft in the United States. Also included are eligibility and knowledge requirements for pilot licensing, and regulations that must be studied to prepare for the FAA written tests for private and commercial pilot certification and for the instrument rating. Includes the following regulations: PART 1 of aviation definitions and abbreviations; PART 61 covering pilot certificates; PART 67 on medical standards; PART 71 for designation of federal airways, controlled airspace, and reporting points; PART 91 of general operating and flight rules; the "new" PART 103 on ultralight flight and vehicles; and NTSB PART 830 covering accident reporting. Also included in this valuable book is a special "Guide to Exam FAR's" for private, commercial, instrument, and flight instructor certificates. Indexed. 176 pages. Printed in regular size, easy-to-read type on 8×10 size pages. Heavy paper covers.

PRIMARY AEROBATIC FLIGHT TRAINING
(With Military Techniques)
by
Arthur S. Medore

Contains the finest "how to" illustrations of basic and advanced aerobatic maneuvers, plus pages of valuable advice pertaining to flying. Maneuvers are presented in the same sequence as they are generally introduced by the instructor during training. There are step-by-step illustrated explanations, and detailed descriptions of each, plus check lists of common errors and control sequences. The instructions are based upon the proven military aerobatic training techniques. A suggested syllabus is included for the instructor's convenience. There are illustrated sections on subjects like "use of instruments", unusual attitude recovery, load factors, flying tailwheel aircraft. Maneuver entry speed charts. This 10¾ × 8¼ size manual includes 160 pages and 133 illustrations. Paperbound.

FLIGHT MANEUVERS MANUAL FOR
INSTRUCTORS & STUDENTS
by Haldon

More than 100,000 sold! Designed to help student pilots learn how to fly the airplane easier and faster, to help all pilots improve their flying skills, and to help standardize training. More than 500 excellent illustrations, many on fold-out pages, of basic and advanced flight maneuvers and procedures. (Most drawings show "low wing" airplanes; see Visualized Flight Maneuvers Handbook for "high wing" airplanes). The maneuvers are illustrated with a special visual technique which enables the reader to follow and understand the flight patterns with ease. Each maneuver is introduced with either outside or instrument references . . . a procedure recommended by the FAA in integrated flight instruction. Also includes a useful glossary of 600 commonly used aviation terms. Spiralbound in durable red vinyl covers. Handy 4½ × 8¼ pocket size.

VISUALIZED FLIGHT MANEUVERS HANDBOOK
by Haldon

The most popular instructional book on maneuvers! Prepared by Harold Holmes, FAA Designated Pilot Examiner and Flight Instructor with over 20,000 hours, it has 520 outstanding drawings and instructions to help student pilots better understand the basic parts of each maneuver. Use before, during, and after flight. A valuable teaching aid for instructors, also an excellent review for licensed pilots preparing for their biennial check rides. A special visual technique is utilized to enable the reader to easily follow and understand the flight patterns. Handy 4¼ × 8 size. (Most illustrations are of high wing airplanes). Spiralbound with blue vinyl covers.

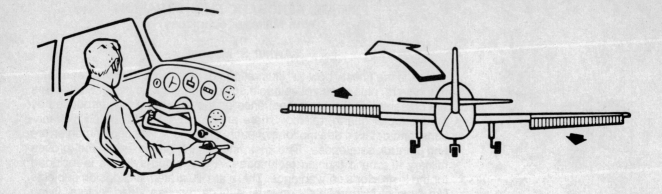

FLIGHT MANEUVERS VIDEO SERIES
by
Video Training Aids, Inc.

New VHS and BETA video cassettes for flight training programs, ground schools, and aviation education classes, as well as home use. Utilizes actual in-flight photography as well as illustrations from the VFM Handbook so that viewer has both cockpit and outside references. (All tapes are sold on a non-returnable basis only).

TAPE I (VID): Aircraft Familiarization, Preflight Operation, Taxiing. (25 minutes).

TAPE II (VID): Normal Takeoff, Straight and Level Flight, Medium Turns, Normal Climbs, Normal Glides and Gliding Turns. (30 minutes).

TAPE III (VID): Flight at Minimum Controllable Airspeed, Elementary Stalls, Takeoff and Departure Stalls, Approach to Landing Stalls. (30 minutes).

TAPE IV (VID): S-Turns Across a Road, Rectangular Pattern, Turns About A Point, 8's Along and Across a Road. (30 minutes).

TAPE V (VID): Go-Around Procedures/Landings, Crosswind Takeoff, The Slip, Crosswind Landing, Short Field Takeoff and Landing, Forced Landing. (30 minutes).

TAPE VI (VID): 720° Power Turns, Steep Turns, 8's Around Pylons, The Chandelle, Spins, Lazy 8's. (30 minutes).

SAVE ON COMBINED TAPES!

TAPE VII (VID): All material from tapes I, II, & III on one 70 minute tape.

TAPE VIII (VID): All material from tapes IV, V, & VI on one 70 minute tape.